NATURE OF LIFE
A STUDY ON MUSCLE

NATURE OF LIFE

A STUDY ON MUSCLE

By

A. SZENT-GYÖRGYI

Department of Biochemistry, University, Budapest

1948

ACADEMIC PRESS INC., PUBLISHERS

NEW YORK, N.Y.

CONTENTS :,

Not long ago I published a little book on Muscular Contraction.* In this book I wanted to record the experiences of my laboratory with muscle after the long years of isolation. I did it mainly for those who wanted to repeat some of our experiments. I struggled with the great bulk of material, stumbling over details, and the resulting book makes poor reading. Therefore, it was a rather welcome invitation when the University of Birmingham and the Massachusetts Institute of Technology invited me for a short series of lectures giving me a chance to sum up my experiences in a more digestible form. This present book contains these lectures, written at Sleepy Hollow, Tarrytown, in an atmosphere of generous American hospitality.

All the electron microscopic (EM) pictures reproduced here are borrowed from M. Staudinger and G. Rózsa's research and are unstained, if not stated otherwise. Technique, data and references may be found in my book.

The following abbreviations will be used:

ATP: Adenosine triphosphate, or adenyl diphosphate.

ADP: Adenosine diphosphate.

AMP: Adenosine monophosphate, or adenylic acid.

DR: Double refraction.

DRF: Double refraction of flow

UW: Unit weight. For myosin and actin 17,600 g. will be taken arbitrarily as UW, whether such units actually exist or not.

MW: Molecular weight.

IP: Isoelectric point.

EM: Electron microscope or E. microscopic.

The research has been started and is being conducted under the auspices of the *Josiah Macy Jr. Foundation, New York.*

April, 1947

*Muscular Contraction. Academic Press, New York, 1947.

FIRST LECTURE

HISTOLOGICAL, MOLECULAR AND ELECTRONIC STRUCTURE
OF MUSCLE

Introduction. Colloidal Chemical Considerations.

The biologist wants to understand life, but life, as such, does not exist: nobody has ever seen it. What we call "life" is a certain quality, the sum of certain reactions of systems of matter, as the smile is a quality or reaction of lips. I cannot take the girl in my right arm and her smile in my left hand and study the two independently. Similarly, we cannot separate life from matter and what we can only study is matter and its reactions. But if we study this matter and its reactions, we study life itself.

Embarking on this adventure our first problem will be the choice of material: which organ and which of its reactions shall we study? In principle it does not matter: any organ or any basic function, if studied properly, will lead us to the understanding of the basic and simple principles of life. In my research I was always guided by the belief that life, however varied in its appearance, is always built on the same simple principles. Caffeine, which produces contracture in muscle, provokes increased nervous activity in brain or flow of urine in the kidney; while veratrine, which causes prolonged contraction in muscle, causes flow of saliva in the salivary gland and prolonged electric response in nerve. If the same keys open different slots, these slots cannot be very much different.

Muscle, as a material of inquiry, offers great advantages. Its function is motion, one of the simplest and oldest signs of life which has always been looked upon by man as the criterion of life. Motion, owing to its mechani-

9

cal character, can be observed with the naked eye and registered by relatively simple means. It is accompanied by very fast and intense chemical changes and changes in energy which can be measured with greater ease and accuracy than the relatively slow functions of parenchymatous organs. All this has made muscle the classical object of biological research and up to the present century the greater half of physiology was muscle-physiology.

I became interested in muscle for another reason. To elaborate, I must poach for a moment on colloidal chemistry. Colloidal particles may have very different shapes; they may be spherical, or form long threads, or anything in between. Their physical properties will depend a great deal on this shape. Spherical particles have little tendency to associate. The geometry of a ball disfavors association and favors inner balance of forces leaving nothing to bind the particles together with. Spherical shape, in colloids, means low viscosity and high motility and nature will apply this form where these qualities are needed (blood serum, milk, etc.). No structures are formed, as a rule, from spherical particles, and you will find it rather difficult to build any mechanism out of marbles.

Contrary to this, elongated particles like threads or rods, have a great tendency to associate and form structures. Such association is favored by the shape, the large surface, the poor balance of forces, and the friction resulting therefrom. Low motility and high viscosity will be characteristic of these particles and nature will invariably resort to this form wherever it wants to build structures. The "structure" of the cell is built of such particles and the really basic biological functions are linked to structure. Particles within this structure are mostly so intimately interlaced, that they cannot be disentangled and isolated without profound damage. If we extract cells or tissues with water, a considerable part, the smaller half of the protein will be dissolved, but it will be the globular

10

proteins only which pass into solution while the basic structure will be left behind in the form of a semi-solid mass. Researchers did not know what to do with it and resolved the difficulty mostly by calling it "residue" and sending it down the sink. Unconsciously, research limited its attention therefore to the easily accessible globular proteins performing rather secondary functions around the basic structure and what we call today "protein chemistry" is, in its greatest part, only the chemistry of globular proteins.

It is in muscle only that, owing to the mechanical nature of its function, we find the particles of the contractile structure arranged in such an orderly fashion which allows us to separate them without denaturation. This gives us the chance to look into the reactions of these structural proteins. Since most of our experiences are derived from globular colloids we will find these reactions rather peculiar if not paradoxical.

Before descending into molecular dimensions let us see what can be learned about muscle by means of the eye, either naked or armed with the microscope.

Microscopic Structure

Mammalian cross-striated muscle consists of fibres of about 0.1 mm. diameter. In essence such fibres are bundles of fibrils of about 0.001 mm. diameter. The greater half of the volume of the fibre is occupied by these fibrils. The muscle contracts because the fibrils contract.

The electron microscope in the hands of Hall, Jacus and Schmitt revealed that the fibrils are bundles of still smaller "filaments." Fig. 1a (Plate I) shows a fibril of the rabbit loosened by supersonic vibration into a very great number of smaller filaments, many microns long, which were thus running continuously through a number of cross-striations. One of these filaments can be seen lying isolated in Fig. 1b (Plate I) under higher magnification.

11

The filaments are the contracting unit of muscle. They are built of a positively doubly-refracting protein. They show no periodic variation of properties and judging by their appearance we would expect the muscle to have a uniformly positive DR. The fact is, however, that "cross-striated muscle" is cross-striated, *i.e.*, has periodically alternating optical properties being composed of strongly doubly-refracting Q and isotropic I segments.

The nature of this cross-striation has given many headaches to research workers and many theories were proposed to explain it. I myself explained it by assigning a spiral structure to fibrils.* None of these theories can be upheld any more in the light of EM examination.

The puzzle has been solved lately by Gerendás and Matoltsy (personal communication) who treated muscle with reagents which dissolved the filaments. The cross-striation persisted but something unexpected happened: the positive double-refracting turned into a negative one and it was the former I discs which were anisotropic now, and the former Q discs which were isotropic. The numerical value of the DR remained equal to the DR of intact muscle but had the opposite sign. These results permit one explanation only: cross-striation is due to the presence of an interfibrillary or interfilamentary substance which has a negative DR and a periodic distribution or orientation compensating in the I discs the positive DR of the filaments. Banga and I have shown many years ago that muscle does contain a negatively doubly-refracting substance which is about 20% of the total protein; in heart muscle it is even more than that. What the meaning and importance of this protein is, and what its relation

*I found that on rotation of the muscle fibre the cross-striation showed a progressive motion from which I concluded that cross-striation can only be an optical illusion and must be due to spiral structure. Gerendas and Matoltsy (personal communication) showed that under conditions of my experiment the cross-striation can be expected to show a progressive motion on rotation but that this motion, too, is an optical illusion.

to filaments is, we do not know. We must not forget that, after all, the muscle fibre is a cell and must have its own protoplasm and this negatively DR protein may be this protoplasm and belong thus, so to say, in the sphere of the private life of the muscle-cell while filaments perform its public functions.

Why this protein, called because of its negative DR N-protein (Gerendás and Matoltsy) has a periodic distribution we do not know. Banga and I have shown that it is a nucleoprotein of the ribose type and has a fibrous structure. G. v. Itterson, and later Bernal and Fankuchen have shown that fibrous colloids, under mechanical stress, may assume periodicity in their orientation (Fig. 2, Plate II). That the periodicity of the N-protein is rather the result of motion of muscle than its cause is supported by the fact that cells in cultures of embryonic heart muscle contract first and develop cross-striation after. Székessy (personal communication) showed that there is a remarkable relation between the diameter of cross-striations, and therefore in the periodicity of the N-protein, and the rate of motion. The rate of motion of different insect-muscles shows very wide variations. While the mandibular muscles of the jaw move with extreme slowness, the leg-muscles move faster, while wing muscles may make several hundred contractions per second. Székessy found that the faster the muscle, the narrower its segmentation. In the mandibular muscles the cross-striation (I+Q band) in different insects, was found to be, on the average, 0.006 mm, while it was 0.004 mm in the leg muscles and 0.002 mm in the wing muscles. In insects which did not fly, thoracic (wing) muscles were found to have a wider striation, similar to that of leg muscles.

We can guess at the physiological importance of the periodic distribution of the N-protein. If this protein were not distributed in a discontinuous way but would fill the interfibrillary or interfilamentary space continuously it would have to be deformed in every contraction. Being a fibrous colloid of high viscosity its rapid deformation would involve considerable expenditure of energy and would impede contraction.

13

Through the discontinuous segmental distribution this is avoided. In contraction the N-protein discs (I segments) are simply brought closer together whereby the Q segment becomes smaller. This explains why it was believed that only the Q segments are contractile. The viscous resistance of a colloid greatly depends on the rate of deformation and one can understand why no such segmental distribution and no cross-striation is present in smooth muscle which slowly works against little resistance. Professor E. Balogh was good enough to show me microscopic slices of lungs of mice infected intranasally with influenza virus. The smooth muscle cells on the small arteries, working against increased resistance, developed cross-striation. (See comm. IV internat. congr. comp. pathol. Rome, 1939, vol. 11, p. 201).

A more profound knowledge concerning this protein may open the way to the understanding of the muscle fibre as a whole. The scope of my present lectures, however, is less ambitious and I will limit myself to the contractile matter of the filaments. The physical properties of muscle will greatly depend on the physical state of this substance. The relatively large amount of globular colloids does not contribute to structure and from the physical point of view we only ask these globular colloids to be corresponding to their shape, mobile, and not to impede motion.

I have mentioned before that we can correlate the physical state of a colloidal system with the shape of its particles. But in muscle the same system has three different physical states. If at rest, muscle is soft and plastic; and if it were not so, we could not be able to move at all. This tells us that the contractile matter is built of relatively short colloidal particles. Contracting muscle is stiff and hard as it has to be if it has to do work indicating long and stiff particles. In relaxation we would expect the muscle to become almost fluid to contain globules instead of threads, the mobility of which facilitates rearrangement into the resting structure without much inner friction.

Nature solved this problem by building the contractile filaments from not one but two colloids. The one I will call myosin. This protein is built of relatively short rods about 2-4,000 A long and 25 A wide, which forms no stiff gel but just a soft plastic mass. The other protein I will call actin, as does its discoverer F. B. Straub. This protein forms long continuous threads which nature has made soft and supple by building them not of long straight peptide chains but of little round balls, globules, which act like ball-bearings. If the two proteins unite, the myosin rodlets attach themselves with the long sides to the actin thread.

The complex, formed of myosin and actin-threads, which we call "actomyosin," has the remarkable property of contractility. Neither of the two components, actin nor myosin, shows any signs of it; but actomyosin is contractile. This can easily be demonstrated by bringing the actomyosin gel, according to the method of H. H. Weber, into the form of threads which have a large surface allowing rapid diffusion of dissolved substances. If we dip such a thread into boiled muscle juice it will contract energetically in a reversible way. Fig. 3a shows such an actomyosin thread, Fig. 3b shows the same thread after it has been suspended for a few seconds in boiled muscle juice. The thread has shrunk to a small volume, and the shrinking is so fast that it gives the impression of active "contraction." Contraction can even be demonstrated in suspensions: the tube in Fig. 3c contained at the outset an apparently homogeneous suspension of actomyosin. On "contraction" the actomyosin precipitated and contracted to a small plug.

This contraction of actomyosin is reversible. By increasing the salt-concentration, upon the addition of NaCl or KCl, the contracted thread can be made to relax, thereby swelling to its original dimensions.

This contraction of actomyosin is very impressive. It is the deepest impression of my research career. It means that this biological function, motion, has been reproduced with constituents of the body outside the living organism.

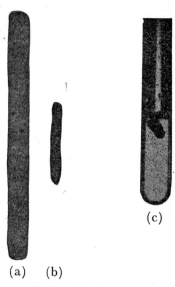

(c)

(a)   (b)

Fig. 3.   (a) Actomyosin thread. (b) The same contracted, magnification 1:30. (c) Contraction of an actomyosin "solution."

Electronic Structure

The changes involved in contraction can satisfactorily
be expressed in terms of colloidal chemistry which deals
with particles as a whole. Contraction and relaxation are
but shrinking and swelling taking place in a structure, a
special geometry.

If, however, we try to explain what happens inside the
particles, we fail. In order to explain the changes taking
place inside the particles during contraction and relaxation, we have to suppose a shift of charges along the myosin particle and uniform decrease of free energy of the
system in its whole extent as well as a uniform distribution
of energy communicated to the system from without. We
have to suppose different actions at a distance, and our
classical chemical concept which pictures the protein mole-

16

cule as built of single peptide chains, the chains built of discrete atoms, does not allow us to explain any such changes or actions. This, our conception of structure, is expressed in the chemical formulae in which the protein is depicted as consisting of separate sub-units, symbolized by letters like C, N, O, H, which means that the system actually is built up of such discrete units consisting of nuclei and their individual electrons. Since no conjugated double bonds or resonating cyclic structures are present in protein, forces cannot be expected to act at greater distances than a few A.

This failure to explain a biological reaction in terms of classical chemistry is not limited to the motion of muscle. I dare say that apart from a very few exceptions* we do not understand *any* biological reaction. Not only can we not explain biological reactions but we can definitely state that those qualities of the system by which it performs these reactions are not expressed in our formulae and thus are not taken account of in our theory of matter. To make this clear let us take any example, say the action of a sexual hormone, a phenanthrene compound. We are now capable of describing the molecules of this substance by a symbol, compiled of strips and C, H and O-s. We describe the protein in the same way. But if we look as chemists do at these formulae we can definitely say that these two substances, phenanthrene and protein will never react. A phenanthrene is a perfectly stable substance which will react chemically only under the most extreme conditions, at high temperature, in concentrated acid or so. In the body this substance produces the most wonderful reactions at a low temperature and in extreme dilution. Moreover there is a disproportionality in the quantity of the active substance and the living system it reacts upon. There are several biological reactions known

*These reactions involve the blocking of certain groups (Cu by cyanide) or their destruction (SH by mono-iodoacetic acid or other reagents).

in which one single molecule induces changes in a whole cell, composed of millions of molecules.

This failure to explain biological phenomena in terms of classical chemistry suggests that there is something wrong with our basic conceptions of structure of living matter, and in order to understand structure and its biological functions we have to look for a new theory of the solid state which allows us to look upon a greater number of molecules as units. Such a theory has been postulated in the last few decades and we have to try to apply it to living structures and see whether it leads us any further in the understanding of biological phenomena.

This new theory of the solid state started out from the study of electric conductivity in metals. It assumes that in a metal, say a piece of wire, the energy-terms of the valency electrons fuse to common bands within which the single electrons have a more or less free motion. They do not belong to single atoms any more but belong to the whole system. The wire conducts electricity by that quality by which a wire is more than the sum of its atoms, which quality cannot be described by current chemical symbols. This theory has later been extended to dielectrics. Dielectrics, like proteins, may have a band-structure without being conducting. Conductivity depends not only on the presence of bands but also on the number of electrons in these bands. If the number of atoms (or other unit cells) is N, the band will be saturated and non-conducting if the number of electrons is 2 N, which will be the case whenever the number of valency-electrons is even. There is no reason, *a priori,* to reject this theory in the case of proteins, provided that the particles possess two basic qualities: 1) there must be a relatively great number of atoms in the system and 2) they must be arranged in space with a very high degree of regularity. As to the first requirement, the number of atoms, the first approximate calculations show that about 10^6 atoms are required which takes us into the region of the size of the smallest viruses. Concerning the regularity of arrangement in space, the recent electron microscope studies of F. O. Schmitt and R. Wyckoff and their associates reveal an amazing regularity. This problem of electric continuity and energy-band structure in proteins has been attacked lately from a different angle with unexpected success. In the polypeptide chain of proteins for every CO there is one NH per amino-acid, the repeating unit of the backbone being NH-C-CO. If each of the CO groups would be linked by an H-bridge to an NH, the resulting NHOC chains could form an equally continuous structure than the NH-C-CO-s of the backbone. This possibility is shown, very schematically, in Fig. 4 where the peptide chain is drawn in a zig-zag which shows that every CO lies close to an NH (R being the side-chain). If these neighboring CO and NH groups were linked by an H-bond we might describe the resulting structure at will as being

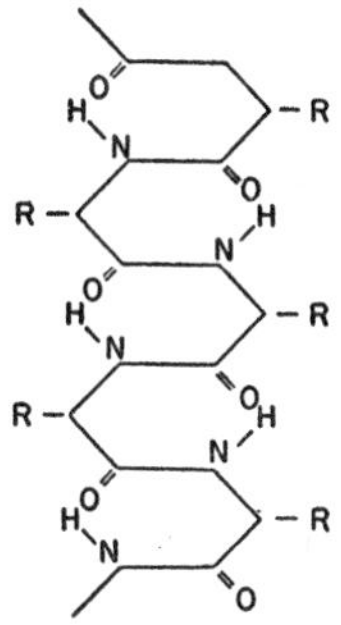

Fig. 4

built of the amino-acid residues NH-C-CO, or describe it as being built of periodically repeating NHOC groups. (The same would hold if the CO and NH groups of neighboring polypeptide-chains were connected by the H-bonds, as assumed by W. T. Astbury and M. L. Huggins.)

19

In earlier studies the single H-bridges have been dealt with as individual units. The bond electrons in the NH and CO were looked upon as localized, the H with its electron only being shared to some extent by the N and CO, giving a low resonance energy of about 6000 cal. Recently, M. G. Evans, J. Gergely and H. B. Ursell (personal communication) attacked the problem along new lines, assigning to the single atoms N, H, O, and C each a mobile electron with no definite localization, but being placed in a molecular orbital. In this conception, the single H-bridges are but members of a higher continuous system with its own high resonance energy. The calculations have shown that, to use Prof. Evans' words, "the electrons in the protein have a certain tendency to non-localization and to occupy levels characteristic of the whole structure. This leads to resonance energy which is lost when its particular configuration of centers in a normal protein is deranged. The bands of levels characteristic of the whole structure are separated and the lower levels completely filled. This means that the structure is nonconducting but may accept electrons in the unfilled levels which would confer semiconductivity on the structure."

This means, in other words, that protein has a band structure and that we can look upon a whole protein particle, and possibly even the system formed by the association of such particles as a single unit, in which, under certain conditions, electrons may have a more or less free mobility. At the same time, we have an explanation of the denaturation, the death of the protein particle, in the breaking up of this continuous band structure.

As will be shown later, the different proteins in our contractile system, i.e., protin and myosin, myosin and actin, are linked together by SH groups. While the electric continuity within the same protein particle is established by means of the system of H-bridges between N and CO, the continuity between different proteins seems to be established by means of H-bridges between S and another hitherto undefined group.

These are only beginnings. Complications will be introduced by the presence of metals and ATP. The energy term of the second electron of Mg, for instance, is at the same level as the higher filled electron band which opens the possibility that this ion takes over an electron from the protein making its band unsaturated and conductant. Ca and Mg may also form chelate rings with NH and CO groups with a high electronic mobility.

Still more fascinating are the complications introduced by the ATP molecules, linked to the myosin. In the animal there is one ATP for every UW of myosin. Without ATP, the actomyosin is unable to give contraction and relaxation and comes to life only by the adsorption of this nucleotide. The deeper knowledge of the mechanism of this role of ATP can be expected to answer one of the greatest mysteries of biology: the function of the nucleic material. The structure of ATP is most fascinating, opening vistas for fantasy along quantum mechanical lines.

If, however, there are bands, electrons must have a statistical distribution in them which distribution might be disturbed by any molecule which is enabled by its specific structure to come close enough and stay there. Band structure may thus open the way to the understanding of biological activity, may lend a deeper meaning to the idea of structure and may explain the fact that oxidative enzymes, which provide the living structure with energy, are linked to structure, while most enzymes, having no such function, are free and globular. We might be able to understand, how the cytochromes, fixed in space with Fe atoms not touching one-another can transmit electrons* and so we might perhaps understand many

*The single cytochromes, in this picture, take the role of metallic impurity in crystals. The different cytochromes with their different redox

21

other things, including growth, which classical biochemistry, a biochemistry of primary valencies, was unable to explain.

My laboratory, in the last few years, was engaged in the study of so-called gelatin-phosphors, in the hope of finding experimental evidence of band structure. Results, in this field, are difficult to interpret. All the same I want to quote some of our experiences. As is generally known, many crystals are phosphorescent, *i.e.*, they emit light if illuminated, even after the illumination has been discontinued. These substances have beeen called crystal-phosphors. This phosphorescence in crystals is explained in many cases by the existence of band spectra. By the absorption of radiant energy electrons are raised to a higher level within these bands and may persist in these higher levels for some time. Eventually they fall back to the lower level emitting the absorbed energy as light again.

It has been known for many decades that gelatin, if dried down with certain dyes, becomes phosphorescent. To distinguish such amorphous phosphors from crystal-phosphors they have been called gelatin-phosphors. Phosphorescence is neither the quality of gelatin nor the quality of the dyes employed and the system becomes phosphorescent through the interaction of both components. My collaborator, J. Boros, measured the conductivity of such systems and found that it increased during illumination, found thus what a physicist would call an inner photoelectric effect, namely, photoelectric conductivity. Such an effect could be taken as evidence for a band structure. Budó, Lukács and Tegzes, however, repeating these experiments and at the same time measuring the temperature of the phosphorescent films found that there was always a thermic effect, the system warmed up, and potentials might be coordinated to definite energy levels and may represent a disturbance which allows electrons to drop to the next lower level liberating their energy piecemeal in a specific mechanism.

with increasing temperature the conductivity increased. The temperature quotient was not high enough to permit the gelatin-phosphors to be classed with semi-conductors, but the thermic effect was high enough to make the interpretation of the results of Boros impossible so that these results cannot be considered any more as independent evidence for the existence of a band structure.

J. Gergely studied other features of gelatin-phosphors. He mixed different substances of low molecular weight with the same dye, for instance, Rhodulin-orange. Many of these substances were found to be phosphorescent, but only if they were crystalline. The better formed the crystals were the more intense was the phosphorescence; and the same substance, if dried down with the dye side by side in crystalline and amorphous condition showed phosphorescence only if present in crystals. This indicates that phosphorescence, induced by dyes, is connected with the regularity of the system and thus possibly with the presence of energy bands. Proteins and high-polymer carbohydrates were the only amorphous substances found which showed this phosphorescence, which seem thus to have within their molecules the required high degree of regularity.

Whatever the explanation of this phosphorescence, its existence shows definitely that protein molecules, like those of gelatin, can enter into very intimate relations with other low-molecular substances, like dyes, to develop some sort of electric structure in common. If these colored phosphorescent gelatin films are wetted they lose phosphorescence and the system is disrupted. In order to obtain information about this effect another protein, casein, was studied somewhat more in detail. Casein, like gelatin, if dried down with Rhodulin-orange, becomes phosphorescent but this phosphorescence is not lost on wetting. It is lost if the concentration of the casein, within the system, drops below 10%. What this limit of

10% means is explained by the study of the DRF. Casein is a globular protein, it can be expected to have a low tendency for association and to have no DRF at low gradients.* If its concentration is raised above 10% it acquires DRF which cannot be due to the orientation of the single particles which are globular, and are not oriented in any way at the low velocity gradients employed. The solution becames doubly refracting because at the high concentration, above 10%, we bring the casein particles in close proximity and force them to associate to bigger, asymmetrical units. DRF, in this case, is an expression of association, which, naturally, is reversible, and disappears on dilution together with the phosphoresence.

This simple experiment shows that the water does not interfere with the link between dye and protein, but interferes with the association of the protein particles. Also the single protein particle, if isolated, shows no phosphorescence, but phosphorescence is readily developed if we bring a greater number of casein particles to association, whereby bigger units are formed. At the same time the experiment shows that a simple association of particles is sufficient to bring about changes in their electronic structure which is necessary for the development of phosphorescence.**

These experiments were extended to other proteins. It was found that the higher the axial asymmetry, the more elongated the particle; thus the greater the tendency for

*Resting solutions of fibrous proteins show no DR since their particles are distributed at random. If stirred, *i.e.*, if a gradient in velocity is established, they become doubly refracting because they become oriented. So, for instance, if a solution of a fibrous colloid is allowed to flow through a capillary tube it will show double refraction because its particles become oriented more or less parallel to the wall. Globular colloids, naturally, do not exhibit such DRF.

**We cannot exclude the idea that association induces phosphorescence by entrapping dyestuff molecules between the associating protein particles. This fixation of the dye molecule would reduce its degree of freedom and make it impossible to get rid of the excess of energy in the form of heat. This possibility, however, seems to be rather remote.

association, the lower the concentration at which phosphorescence appears. While in the globular casein the limit was 10%, in the elongated myosin it was 0.2%. Phosphorescence always went hand in hand with DRF, which, in the case of myosin also is an expression of association. If a myosin-dye solution [which because of its high dilution, gave no DRF and no phosphorescence], was mixed with a dilute fibrous actin solution, [which, due its dilution, had no DRF or phosphorescence either], there appeared DRF and phosphorescence, because of the formation of the highly fibrous and highly associated actomyosin. If the actomyosin was brought to dissociation the DRF and phosphorescence disappeared again. In all these experiments it was always the phosphorescence which disappeared first, followed immediately by the disappearance of DRF showing that there is no phosphorescence without association and that association of protein particles means more than proximity.

My reason for tarrying so long at this topic is that "myosin," too, which is a chromoprotein, contains a dye. This is the more remarkable because, as I will show later, this dye is located at the point where the ATP is split, its energy liberated. The dye is involved in this process with its two labile electrons and is active only if it has these two electrons. This suggests that it is these two electrons of the dye which in the first instance take up the energy, liberated by splitting the pyrophosphate bond, transmitting it to the protein. The ultimate food of the living system is the excited electron, its excess energy. It seems quite possible that the most primitive form of life was some such system in which radiant energy was directly put on to the protein by a dye. Later the system might have learned how to store energy of radiation in the form of foodstuff-molecules and then put the energy of the foodstuff on the protein structure. This way the participation of a dye in muscular contraction or in energy-liberating

25

metabolic processes in general, may still be the remains of such a primitive mechanism.

I am aware that these experiments on phosphorescence are rather obscure, and perhaps I should have omitted them altogether. The first steps, in a new field, are always difficult and the quantum mechanical approach of biological phenomena is a field where there are but very few footprints. The analysis of muscular activity has led us into a new domain. The scientist, when analyzing phenomena of life, often fares like the holy man who very much wanted to know what is inside Heaven and prayed hard that he might be permitted to see it. One day Heavens opened up to him and he could look inside and what had he seen?: another Heaven.

SECOND LECTURE

Myosin and Actin

Introduction

As described in the previous lecture, actomyosin can be brought to contraction by dipping it into boiled muscle juice. In order to understand this reaction, we must know all about its components, we must know all about myosin, actin, and we must know what substances of the boiled juice are involved in this reaction. The last question is the simplest, and analysis has shown that there are three substances in the extract which play a part: potassium ions, magnesium ions, and ATP. ATP is the abbreviation of adenosine-triphosphate, a complicated organic molecule containing an adenylic group, a carbohydrate and three phosphoric groups, two of which at least, are linked together by a phosphoric-anhydride link. The participation of this substance in this reaction is remarkable for several reasons. According to our present knowledge the phosphoric-anhydride link is the source of the energy of the muscular contraction. In order to establish such a link we must invest 11,000 calories, which will be liberated again, if the link is broken; and the link is broken in contraction and supplies the energy needed. But the participation of ATP is remarkable for another reason too. As far as we know the basic living structures, performing basic biological functions, are all nucleoproteins. Life in its essence seems to be dependent on this combination of nucleic acid and protein, and actomyosin would be the first exception. But as I will show later, ATP has two functions. Apart from being the source of energy it is also a building-block of the system. About 70 molecules of ATP are attached to every myosin particle and without this ATP myosin would do just nothing, though it is only one ATP molecule which has to be split in one contraction; the rest are not touched but have to be there in order to make myosin reactive. ATP is a nucleotide, a substance closely related to nucleic acid, and seems to play the same role in actomyosin as nucleic acid does in other structures.

Probably the muscle cannot permit itself to have long nucleic acid molecules which would interfere with its mechanical function. So in muscle the nucleic acid is cut up into small fragments and attached in this form to the myosin, and it is these small pieces of nucleic acid which we actually call ATP, and the contractile substance of muscle is, after all, a nucleoprotein (or more exactly a nucleotidoprotein): a compound of ATP and actomyosin.

Myosin

Myosin is a hydrophilic colloid which readily dissolves in water, giving a clear solution. It crystallizes readily at about pH 6.5 (Fig. 5, Plate II) in presence of 0.025 M KCl. It can be recrystallized readily without changing properties. In the electric field (O. Snellman and T. Erdös)[*] it behaves as a homogeneous substance if dissolved in 0.5 M KCl. Its MW is between $1-1,5.10^6$ g. (Weber and Stöver, Schramm and Weber,[**] Snellman and Erdös[*]).

On recrystallization, subtler properties, like enzymic activity, remain unchanged so we have reason to talk about myosin as about a well defined substance.

Its viscosity is not too high and normal; it corresponds to the viscosity of polyvinyl alcohol of an axial ratio of

[*]Personal communication.
[**]Letter from Professor H. H. Weber, December 21, 1946,

1:200. Axial ratios of the same order have been deduced from diffusion and sedimentation constants by Schramm and Weber, and Snellman and Erdös. This means that myosin consists of elongated particles of about 2,000-4,000 A in length and about 25 A in diameter which corresponds roughly to the shape of a stick made of 10 matches stuck together and placed end to end;* accordingly, the viscosity of myosin solutions is moderate. It forms no stiff elastic gels; at high concentration it forms a soft plastic mass.

Its particles, if discharged, associate side by side. The beautifully crystalline needles turn out, if examined by the EM to be such aggregates (Fig. 6a, Plate III). The ends of the crystal split up like a brush and fizzle out to nothing, the single myosin particle being too thin to be seen (limit of resolving power 50 A).

If the crystallization is conducted in such a way as to give very small crystals (Fig. 6b, Plate III) the EM will reveal a great number of very fine and small needles of different length. These needles are so delicate that they can be only composed of a relatively small number of units. What is remarkable in these needles is that the finest of them have mostly a length of 2000-4000 A, the length calculated for the single myosin particle. At this length as the charges of myosin particles are neutralized and repulsive forces diminished the particles approach one another,

*Weber and Stöver have found that on treating myosin with a strong urea solution the particles broke up into smaller units of MW of the order 10^5 g. Guba has found that on treatment with urea the viscosity of myosin fell to the viscosity of globular proteins thus corroborating Weber and Stöver. These observations suggested that the myosin particle is built of a number of smaller globular units. Erdös, however, working on the ultracentrifuge, found that the major part of the myosin particles does not go to pieces in urea, it simply curls up to a globule. If the urea was not allowed to act for too long a period this coiling up was reversible, and on elimination of the urea the myosin particles stretched out again. This reaction is of great biological interest.

associating, evidently, side by side.* The EM pictures show clearly that the great bulk of water present in crystalline myosin is located between the needles, and myosin particles themselves have a very low inherent affinity for water. Their behavior is mainly governed by charges and the resulting repulsion.

In spite of the physical uniformity of its particles, myosin has a rather complex structure and could be called rather a "system" than a "substance,"almost a small living organism. As revealed by the study of its enzymic activities, it is composed of an inactive skeleton to which are attached a number of globular proteins which greatly modify the physical properties of the skeleton and make the system enzymatically active. The first enzymic activity of "myosin" was described by Engelhardt and Ljubimowa, who showed that "myosin" could detach one phosphate from ATP splitting the pyrophosphate-link. Later Laki, Banga and Guba's work made it evident that "myosin" is capable of detaching a second phosphate from ATP as well, while Banga has shown that "myosin" also deaminates ATP and deaminates ADP (adenosine-diphosphate), all these reactions being independent enzymic functions.

Without its attached globular proteins myosin is entirely inactive. It has no enzymic function and does not contract in presence of actin; it forms no stable compound with actin. The globules are equally inactive in themselves and it is only the system containing the two, skeleton and globules, which is active. The globules, involved in enzymic reaction (dephosphorylation, deamination) with ADP, are relatively easily detached from the skeleton, while those involved in reaction with ATP are attached rather strongly.

---

*There seems to be a regular arrangement of particles even before the formation of visible particles, as indicated by the silky sheen displayed on stirring.

One is rather at a loss as to what to call "myosin" now. Old "myosin" of earlier authors has turned out to be an actomyosin of varying composition, the main characteristics of which were water insolubility and DRF if dissolved in a strong salt-solution. New "myosin" is water soluble and has no DRF. I retained the name as homage to the earlier workers. But what shall we call "myosin" now? The whole system, skeleton, globules and all? But the globules are detached with different degrees of ease and "myosin" cannot be a homogeneous substance even if it behaves as such in the ultracentrifuge or in the Tiselius.

The globules, if isolated, have quite extraordinary properties: they are not destroyed by 1 N HCl and can be boiled in impure solution in 0.1 N HCl without loss of activity for a quarter of an hour.* The first protein, studied somewhat more closely, turned out to be a chromoprotein, a compound of hitherto unknown fluorescent dye and a protein, and it seems probable that other members of this group are built likewise. These globules thus deserve a name for themselves. In my laboratory we call them "protins" to distinguish them from other proteins. In order to avoid confusion and the necessity of creating new names for the individual protins we characterize them by their action "ATP-P-protin" being the protin involved in the splitting off of the first phosphate from ATP. "ADP-P-protin" is the protin involved in the splitting off of phosphate from ADP. The "ATP-N-protin" is involved in the deamination of ATP, the ADP-N-protin" in the deamination of ADP. The "ATP-c-protin" is the protin without which there is no contraction in actomyosin on addition of ATP, "ADP-c-protein" being the corresponding protin for ADP. What relation these "c"-protins have to the "P"-protins remains to be shown.

*H. Kalckar's myokinase has similar properties. The first thermostable enzyme, in muscle, was described by Curtius and Ohlmeyer in O. Meyerhof's laboratory.

The meaning of the name "myosin" becomes, under these conditions, somewhat doubtful and already I have been reproached by colleagues for having confused the nomenclature in this field. It is not the nomenclature, it is the facts which are bewildering. There are even reasons to believe that the list of our troubles is not complete yet and nature is not prepared to fit into our ideas. "Myosin" contains lipoidic matter, too. In the one experiment made I found 3%, partly acetone soluble, partly acetone insoluble. That this lipoidic matter is not solely a fortuitous admixture has been shown by the isolation of a crystalline cerebroside from this lipoidic matter. F. Guba found that it is possible to separate myosin from this cerebroside, but if separated it would not contract any more (in the presence of actin) on addition of ADP, but would do so if the cerebroside is restored to it. If "myosin" is characterized by contractility (in presence of actin) then, evidently, we have to include the cerebroside in its structure. According to this conception, "myosin" denotes a level of organization rather than a substance; a level which, fortunately, can be characterized by certain physical constants. The great importance of sexual hormones, other steroids and related substances for muscle and its development is well known from physiology and sooner or later we will have to fit these (and maybe other substances as well) into this picture.

Absorption of Ions

However rich and colorful life may appear, in its lowest levels of organization, when we get down to the dimension of molecules, it is only atoms, ions, electrons and charges, and so we must give special attention to the latter.

Myosin has its IP at 5.3, having therefore at neutral reaction a negative charge, derived mainly from the predominating dissociation of carboxylic groups. The number of these charges can be calculated approximately from the dissociation curve of myosin. The dissociation curve of myosin is not established yet in a fully satisfactory manner. The dissociation curve obtained by M. Dubuisson and Dubuisson and Hamoir suggests about 2.5 charges for every UW of myosin at pH 7. Accordingly, myosin, dissolved in neutral water, is anodic. If, however, a small quantity of a neutral salt like KCl is added to this solution, the myosin is precipitated quantitatively and loses its charge. This reaction, for a hydrophilic colloid, is quite unique. Its mechanism is revealed by the studies of Banga, completed later by W. S. Hermann, which showed that this precipitation and loss of charge is due to the specific adsorption of cations, 3 K ions being adsorbed at pH 7.4 by every UW of myosin from KCl neutralizing the original negative charge.

Before going further, we must stop for a minute at this point and discuss "neutralization." Neutralization generally means that positive and negative charges unite and the positively charged particles take over electrons from the negative ones. Neutralization, in this case, cannot mean this; the K ions cannot possibly take over the negative charge of the COO groups and can form no undissociated salts with it.* Neutralization, in this case, can mean no more than that the positive K ions are held by the negative myosin particle in some unknown way and that the positive charge of the K ion neutralizes the outward action of the negative charge and there is no net negative charge now; in relation to an external field the K-myosin compound is isoelectric. This being so, the myosin par-

---

*It seems possible that the negative charge of the dissociated COO is not located at this group but is shared by the whole protein particle. We could, in this case, talk only of the probability of the electron's being found at this point. This could perhaps explain why these negative charges (being mobile) are better balanced by the adsorbed K ions than are the more localized charges acquired by the adsorption of Cl ions (see later).

ticles no longer repel each other and associate. They approach each other at the measure as charges are "neutralized" and associate forming needles when the charge is at a minimum.

At approximately neutral reaction this minimum is reached in the presence of 0.025 M KCl. Up to this point no Cl ions are adsorbed. If we increase the KCl concentration to 0.1 M the myosin dissolves again which indicates that it is recharged. The analysis shows (Fig. 7) that

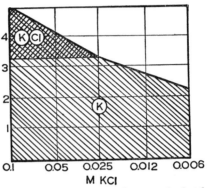

Fig. 7.   Fixation of K and Cl ions by myosin in the presence of varied concentrations of KCl at pH 7.4. Ordinate: equivalents of K or Cl bound by the UW (17,600 g.) of myosin. In the singly hatched zone only K is bound. In the doubly hatched zone K and Cl are bound in equivalent quantities.

now it adsorbs K ions even more intensely than before, but adsorbs at the same time an equivalent quantity of Cl ions. The net charge thus remains approximately zero. The rapidly increasing solubility indicates that these charges are poorly balanced. We can thus distinguish between two zones of absorption. The curves of both are, on a logarithmic scale, straight lines but have different gradients. In the "primary zone", which extends in the case of KCl at neutral reaction from 0-0.025 M KCl, K+ only is adsorbed, and "neutralizes" the negative charge of the protein. In this zone, these negative charges are well balanced

34

by the positive charges acquired by the adsorption of K-ions, which results in the precipitation, i. e., association of the particles. In the "secondary zone", above 0.025 M KCl, there is no net charge acquired, but the positive and negative charges, due to the adsorption of K *and* Cl ions, are poorly balanced which causes repulsion of particles and dissolution. Two positive and two negative charges per UW are sufficient to bring myosin into solution. The physical properties of myosin are governed by charges which also play a basic role in this change of physical state expressing itself in "contraction." The knowledge of the forces responsible for the adsorption of ions is of basic importance. At present, we know next to nothing of them and can hardly guess at their nature. What we can state about them is rather negative: that the forces of adsorption are more or less independent of the dissociation of the COOH and NH2 groups, though the negative charge of the particle will favor adsorption of positive ions and will prevent the adsorption of negative ones. This is clearly borne out by the adsorption of ions by myosin at its isoelectric point, at pH 5.3. Fig. 8 shows the adsorption of K ions at different pHs. The top curve is at pH 7.5. Up to the breaking point at 0.025 M KCl only K ions are adsorbed. Here the myosin has no longer a net negative charge and from now on K and Cl ions are adsorbed in equivalent quantity if the KCl concentration is further increased. The curve 5.3 shows the K adsorption at pH 5.3, the IP of myosin. The slope of the curve is equally steep here as at pH 7.5, thus the adsorption is equally intense, but the curve lies somewhat lower because there was no negative charge at the beginning to promote the adsorption of K ions. The myosin adsorbs from the beginning K and Cl ions in equivalent quantities. The IP, in this case pH 5.3, means minimum of dissociation of COOH and NH_2 groups. As shown by the gradient, the adsorption is equally intense as at other pH's. Adsorption of ions is therefore not due to the dissociated COOH or NH_2 groups, though the negative charge gained by the former promotes the adsorption of positive

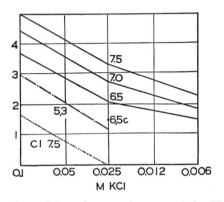

Fig. 8. Fixation of ions by myosin at varied pH. Ordinate: equivalents of ions bound by the UW of myosin. Full lines: fixation of K; upper broken line: fixation of K and fixation of Cl; lower broken line: fixation of Cl at pH 7.5. The point 6.5c indicates the quantity of K bound in 0.025 M KCl at pH 6.5 after subtraction of the quantity equivalent to the Cl bound simultaneously.

ions and prevents that of negative ones; but this has only a modifying effect and the adsorption itself is not due to these dissociating groups.

There is a great difference in the affinity of myosin for different ions. Myosin seems to be unable to distinguish between K and Na ions, but the affinity for these ions is greatly exceeded by the affinity for bivalent Mg^{++} and this again by the affinity for Ca^{++}. Therefore, if all these ions are offered simultaneously it will be the Ca^{++} which is adsorbed first and to the greatest extent; then comes Mg^{++} and finally K^+ and Na^+. Correspondingly, in order to neutralize the negative charge of myosin, we need the highest concentration of KCl or NaCl (0.025 M), less $MgCl_2$ (0.012 M) still less $CaCl_2$ (0.006 M). According to the analysis of Dubuisson, muscle contains 0.101 M K and

36

some Na, 0.012 M Mg and 0.006 M Ca. (Hill and Kupalow's values are very similar).

These data admit an important conclusion about myosin in muscle. It is generally believed that our body is built mainly of anodic, negatively charged colloids, the IP of proteins being mostly in the acid region. As far as myosin shows, the protein must be approximately neutral, the negative charge originating from the prevalent dissociation of COOH groups being compensated by the adsorption of cations. This neutralization will be done by Ca and Mg ions, chiefly by Mg^{++}, very little Ca^{++} being present. (This small amount of Ca^{++} is probably adsorbed by actin, which protein seems to have a similar story but has a higher affinity for Ca^{++} than myosin.) There is just enough Mg^{++} to neutralize the myosin, but definitely not enough to occupy the primary zone. Only K^{+}, together with Na^{+}, is present in sufficiently high concentration to be adsorbed in the secondary zone. According to the ionic concentrations in muscle three alkali metal ions can be expected to be adsorbed in the secondary zone. In this zone the adsorption is rather loose, as indicated by the steepness of the curve of adsorption, which means that slight changes in the ionic concentration in the solvent lead to release or adsorption of ions in this zone. Sudden changes in the physical properties of the myosin can therefore be expected to be induced by changes in the secondary zone of adsorption, either through the release of ions or their better balancing of each other. As indicated by the relative flatness of the curve, ions are held much tighter in the primary zone and so changes in adsorption are less probable to occur in this zone. No rapid change in physical state of the myosin can be expected anyway to be caused in this region, charges being balanced here much better than in the secondary zone.

My previous statement that myosin is "discharged" by KCl and has no net charge is not completely correct.

Erdös,* measuring charges in the Tiselius found myosin dissolved in o.5 M KCl at neutral reactions, still weakly electro-negative, and on first thought, one would be inclined to ascribe this weak charge (three elementary charges per molecule on first approximation) to an incomplete neutralization of the original negative charge of the protein. This assumption, however, is incorrect. Like KCl CaCl$_2$ has an analogous effect on the physical state of myosin $i.e.$, small concentrations of it discharge and precipitate while larger concentrations recharge and redissolve. There is a break in the curve at the maximum precipitation and above this point positive and negative charges are adsorbed in equivalent quantities. The myosin, brought into solution again, now has a positive charge which cannot be due to the incomplete neutralization of the charge of myosin, which was negative. This shows that salts, adsorbed to the myosin in the secondary zone, can lend to it a new charge of their own. This charge is opposite in the case of Ca^{++} and alkali metals. We do not know how this charge is generated. K. Laki studying the shift of the isoelectric point of casein in the presence of salts found that this could be correlated with the differences in electronegativity of the cation and anion present. Possibly the positive charge lent to the myosin by Casalts and the negative charge lent to it by alkali metal salts may have some such origin. But whatever its origin it may have very great biological importance and is perhaps connected with the classical equilibration of ions. We have previously seen that a negative charge of the myosin helps the adsorption of positive particles and repels negative ones. The whole behavior of the protein may be tuned by some such basic charge, and may explain the ionic antagonisms which have even been connected with antagonisms of the sympathetic and parasympathetic nervous sys-

*Personal communication.

tem. Anyway, these charges are a most fascinating problem. The energy term of the second electron of Ca^{++} and Mg^{++} are much lower than those of K^+ and Na^+, and it is not impossible that bivalent ions actually accept one electron from the protein.

Myosin is precipitated in the absence of salts by acids at its isoelectric point, pH 5.3. If it is precipitated in the presence of 0.025 M KCl at pH 7 or 7.5, it means an extreme extension of the isoelectric pH zone. Shift and extension of this zone by salts is also observed in another protein like casein and was the subject of my first chemical paper, prepared under the guidance of L. Michaelis. The ionic adsorption of myosin is thus qualitatively a general property of proteins. Myosin is unique in the extent of this adsorption. Nature seems to use no new principles in creating life, it only emphasizes them according to its specific ends.

Adsorption of ATP

Up to this point we have discussed mainly the adsorption of cations. There is one anion in muscle of special interest: ATP. It is a tetravalent anion but at neutral reaction only three out of the four acidic groups are dissociated, so we may consider it as trivalent. As a trivalent anion it may be expected to have a strong adsorbability. With our experience hitherto collected, we can, to some extent, predict what will happen if ATP is added to myosin. In the absence of KCl or other salts myosin will be anodic and will not adsorb ATP at all. On addition of KCl, we may expect it to be adsorbed in proportion to the quantity of K^+ adsorbed and the logarithm of the KCl-concentration. This is actually what the experiments of Banga and Hermann have shown. ATP will have no precipitating or dehydrating action whatever because it will be adsorbed in the secondary zone only and will tend to recharge the myosin. Thus ATP inhibits the precipitation of myosin by KCl. ATP only charges and hydrates myosin. Its adsorption, in the presence of KCl, is fairly strong but not at all striking.

Results became more striking and unexpected when, similarly to conditions in muscle, the negative charge of myosin was neutralized, the primary zone being occupied by bivalent ions, Ca^{++} or Mg^{++}. This isoelectric Ca or Mg-myosinate still does not adsorb ATP at all. If, however KCl is added now in sufficient concentration to be bound in the primary zone, adsorption becomes excessive (W. Sz. Hermann). With increasing K ion concentration, the adsorption of ATP rises rapidly to reach a sharp maxi-

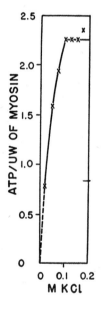

Fig. 9. Adsorption of ATP in the presence of 0.0005 M $CaCl_2$ and varied concentrations of KCl (abscissa). Ordinate: mols of ATP adsorbed by every 17,600 g. of myosin in the presence of 0.02% ATP. The broken line is extrapolated for 0 M KCl.

mum (Fig. 9) in a critical way. This means not only that the adsorption of K+ in the secondary zone causes ATP to be absorbed, but it also means that in the critical region

40

release of absorbed K^+ must cause a sudden release of adsorbed ATP. There seems to be a stoichiometric relation between the number of K^+ and ATP molecules adsorbed. In the different experiments 1-2 K^+ seem to be necessary to entail the adsorption of one ATP. In muscle there is much K^+ and little ATP and the UW of myosin keeps 3 K ions adsorbed for every ATP molecule. This means that this ATP molecule must be held very tightly and in muscle there is no free ATP at all.

Ca and Mg ions, adsorbed in the primary zone, thus change the properties of the myosin particle in such a way that it will become a strong adsorbent of ATP if it acquires the necessary positive charge by the adsorption of K ions. K ions adsorbed in the primary zone have no such effect. Which ion neutralizes the negative charge of the myosin is therefore important. Considering ions simply as charged balls does not meet the facts. Possibly the bivalent ions, if adsorbed in the primary zone and supported by the electrostatic attraction of the K^+ in the secondary zone, are also instrumental in binding ATP to the protein, the great affinity of polyphosphates to bivalent ions being known from inorganic chemistry. F. Buchthal found the UV spectrum of ATP, adsorbed to myosin, was altered which shows that the purine end of the nucleotide is also involved in the mechanism of adsorption; and ATP, by its purine group, enters into some very close relation to the protein.

Enzymatic Properties of Myosin

As mentioned previously, the "myosin" particle has at least four different enzymatic activities, linked to the adsorbed protins, while the rod-shaped skeletal substance is inactive. In resting muscle, about 70 ATP molecules are kept adsorbed to the skeleton but only the ATP molecules coming in touch with the protins will be attacked

41

enzymatically. In Fig. 10 this is shown schematically in a very rough and tentative way. (We have no data of the number, distribution, and dimensions of the protin particles.)

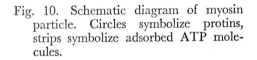

Fig. 10. Schematic diagram of myosin particle. Circles symbolize protins, strips symbolize adsorbed ATP molecules.

To date only one of the protins has been isolated to some extent, the ADP-P-protin (F. Guba). This is a chromoprotein, a compound of the protin and a hitherto-unknown dye. The compound is active only if the dye is present in its reduced form, *i.e.,* has both of its labile electrons. The dye can be detached from the protin by treatment with dilute acetone, which suggests H bonds between the dye and the protin.

In the linking of the protin to the skeletal substance of myosin SH groups are involved. If the SH's are oxidized, no link can be established between the two.

One very remarkable point is the influence of actin on the affinity between skeleton and protin. Actin very greatly increases this affinity; even one actin globule of MW 76,000 per myosin particle of MW 10^6 g. has a strong effect which may explain why actin enhances certain enzymatic reactions of myosin.

What lends special interest to these relations is the possibility that these influences may work both ways, and as the actin greatly alters the affinity of skeleton to protin, so changes taking place on the protin may induce changes in the relation of actin and myosin and the physical state of their actomyosin.

Discussing the enzymatic activities of "myosin," we must be reminded that there probably is no such thing as free myosin in muscle. Myosin is just a cogwheel in a higher organization; isolated myosin, severed from its natural relations and inhibitions, might have quite different qualities. Isolated myosin is an enzyme turned loose which readily dephosphorylates ATP without rhyme or reason, dissipating its energy as heat. Enzymes like pepsin are made to split their substrate as fast and as completely as possible. In muscle it is equally important that the system should not split ATP at certain moments as it is important that it should do so at others. We must always remember the level of organization we are at when we study biological reactions. We will come back later to this point.

The enzymatic activity depends on charges. Salt-free negatively charged myosin is enzymatically inactive. Accordingly, for every salt that does not denature myosin, there is a definite maximum of activity. With KCl the maximum is between 0.1-0.6 M. Above 2 M KCl the myosin becomes inactive. Not all ions are equally active; thus it is not simply a question of charges. Of the cations Ca^{++} is the best, the second best being Mg^{++}.

According to Singher and Barron myosin, as ATP-ase, is an SH-enzyme. In our experience myosin, with all its free SH-s blocked, is still about half as active as native myosin in dephosphorylating ATP. This indicates that the SH-groups are not involved in this enzymic activity.

Actin has the striking property of being capable of existing in globular as well as in fibrous form. It can be extracted from tissues only after it has been liberated from its connections and depolymerized into globules. G-actin (G referring to "globular") is a typical globular protein of very low and normal viscosity. According to its discoverer F. B. Straub, it has a MW of 76,000. According to its tryptophane content its minimum MW is 76,000 and it passes through collodion filters which keep back hemoglobin and partly egg albumin. Its probable MW is therefore about 76,000 which brings its dimensions below the resolving power of current electron microscopes.

Fig. 11a (Plate IV) is an EM picture of globular actin (G. Rózsa and M. Staudinger). The spots are aggregates the size of which is different down to the limit of visibility. What is noteworthy on this picture is the fact that everything that can be seen is round, indicating a globular shape. Elongated particles tend to associate to elongated agglomerates. Fig. 11b (Plate IV) is the same actin after polymerization. It shows a definitely fibrous character. In Fig. 12 (Plate V) the actin is caught in the process of its polymerization and one can see threads and globules side by side. Fig. 13 (Plate V) gives information about the unit of fibrous actin. It shows long threads of uniform diameter, similar to the threads in the EM pictures of Hall of Jacus.

This last picture in Fig. 13 is gold-shadowed. What is surprising in such pictures of actin is the narrowness of the shadow. The preparation, in this case, was shadowed from an angle which would have to make the shadow ten times wider than the height of the particle. In the picture the shadows are approximately of the same diameter as the threads themselves which must thus be very flat, 1/10 as high as they are wide. It is difficult to understand how a solid protein particle can flatten to this extent.

Lately Dr. Rózsa has obtained pictures in which the actin-threads show a spiral structure with a periodicity of 400 A. Similar periodicity was observed in actomyosin threads and seemed to decrease on contraction. I hope to find an opportunity to have this very important point reinvestigated with a higher resolving power.

The association into threads and dissociation into globules is an entirely reversible process which is nicely shown by Figs. 14a and b (Plate VI). Fig. 14a (Plate VI) shows the EM picture of a fibrous actin preparation after 10 minutes treatment with ultrasonic radiation which disintegrates the fibres into globules. One sees in this picture that one sees nothing. (The big black spots have to be discounted.) Fig. 14b (Plate VI) shows the same preparation after standing for ten minutes. Most fibres shown in this picture are rough agglomerates but one can also see fibres of very thin, uniform diameters representing the elementary unit.

Under special conditions actin may polymerize also to shorter rods (Fig. 15, Plate VII). According to Hall and Jacus, the length of particles is a function of pH.

Judged by the length of particles, actin should have a rather high viscosity and should readily form elastic gels. In fact its viscosity is relatively low, of the same order as that of myosin, and actin forms no gels at all. Perhaps the explanation of this anomaly lies in a great flexibility of the thread due to being built of globular particles, held together by relatively weak forces, which act as ball bearings. Actin is thixotropic, which means that forces are not completely balanced by this association. We can expect the thread to have unbalanced forces, otherwise it could not unite with myosin to form actomyosin.

Association of actin is a matter of charge. At a somewhat alkaline reaction and in the absence of salts the fibres

45

depolymerize into globules. To make the globules polymerize again one must add a little salt, about 0.1 M KCl. In the complete absence of Mg^{++} there is no polymerization at all, and within limits the rate of polymerization depends on the concentration of Mg^{++} present (Straub). Actin is capable of binding very firmly one or two Mg^{++} and one Ca^{++} per UW. The situation seems to be analogous to that of myosin. The results of Straub and Erdös suggest that 6 equivalents of metal are needed per UW for the neutralization of the original negative charge. Actin has a very great affinity for bivalent ions and is precipitated by their low concentration. Evidently, the bivalent cation is bound very strongly in the primary zone and precipitates the molecule by rendering it electroneutral. Actin, prepared by the newer method of Guba and Straub contains 1 Ca per UW, *i.e.*, 4 Ca per molecule. Without this Ca the actin is very unstable and deteriorates quickly (Straub).

The affinity for alkali metals is much lower. While 0.001 M Ca^{++} will induce polymerization (if Mg^{++} is present), 0.1. M KCl 1 or NaCl is needed to produce the same effect. But here again the individuality of the ions plays a considerable role, as shown by Straub, in a very fascinating way. The effects observed recall all the features of physiological ionic equilibration. While both 0.005 M $CaCl_2$ and 0.1 M NaCl induce rapid polymerization, if added simultaneously they will have no effect at all. They mutually balance each other, showing that polymerization is not simply a question of charge, but that subtler qualities of ions are involved. Similar effects can be observed in solubility; $CaCl_2$ precipitates, NaCl redissolves actin. Still more intriguing is the relation of K^+ and Na^+. KCl acts like NaCl but is somewhat less active in inducing polymerization. O.1 M NaCl is active and a small change in its concentration will not matter, so one would expect that the addition of a little KCl to this O.1 NaCl will have no

46

effect at all. All the same, this addition of 0.002 M KCl will increase the rate of polymerization duplicating the well-known physiological equilibration of K^+ and Na^+.

The polymerization of actin is not only fascinating, but it is complicated too. Its kinetics can be measured in the viscosimeter, F-actin being more viscous than G-actin. If the actin is well prepared and preserved, it polymerizes according to an autocatalytic type, which means that there is a latent period and for a while apparently nothing happens. Then the polymerization sets in and proceeds to completion at a very high rate. Accordingly, Erdös finds in actin either very high or very low sedimentation constants, but nothing in-between. The process differs in one respect from other autocatalytic reactions: it is not accelerated upon the addition of traces of the product, F-actin. The polymerization process is not helped by adding long threads. Apparently all the threads must reach a certain critical length before rapid polymerization sets in.

When Ca and Na balance each other they act merely by lengthening the latent period, but once the polymerization sets in it proceeds at the same high rate, as when Na^+ or Ca^{++} is the only ion present.

The inner mechanism of polymerization seems to be rather complicated. As mentioned before, there is no polymerization at all without Mg^{++}. Apart from traces of Mg^{++} we need another ion in higher concentration: Ca^{++}, Mg^{++}, Na^+ or K^+, or any other cation that does not denature the protein. If oxidized, actin does not polymerize any more, but can be reactivated by reduction by cysteine or ascorbic acid. The oxidizable group which is also auto-oxidizable, is not SH (Straub). Actin, with all its SH-s blocked, is still capable of polymerization (Guba). According to Straub, actin also has a prosthetic group which can be detached and without which there is no polymerization. Professor Straub is engaged at present in its isolation. The rate of polymerization depends also on

47

the actin-concentration. Polymerization is greatly catalyzed at lower, physiological salt concentrations by myosin, while it is entirely inhibited by myosin in 0.5 M KCl. Putting all this together, we may say that it is possible that the polymerization of actin in muscle may occur with exceeding rapidity and may therefore take place in every cycle of contraction.

THIRD LECTURE

Actomyosin

Actomyosin, Salts and ATP

If a solution of myosin and F-actin are mixed, the sudden rise of viscosity indicates that a reaction has taken place: a new substance, actomyosin, has been formed through the union of two proteins. The viscosity is now high and anomalous, and the new substance behaves as a typical fibrous high polymer. The high double refraction of flow found by Edsall and von Muralt in "myosin" is a quality of the actomyosin present. The DRF of actomyosin is higher than it would be corresponding to its actin content, and myosin alone, at higher salt concentrations, has no DRF at all. Actomyosin can be prepared not only by putting actin and myosin together, but also directly from muscle by means of prolonged extraction. The EM reveals the presence of long threads (Fig. 16, Plate VII) which seem to be somewhat thicker and more discrete than those of actin. They are evidently actin threads coated with myosin particles running lengthwise. They cannot be distinguished from the filaments of the muscle fibril (Fig. 1a, Plate I). Since the actin threads were very long before the addition of myosin, the rise of viscosity on mixing actin and myosin cannot be explained by the lengthening of particles, but should probably be explained by the increased stiffness and cohesion of the actomyosin threads. Actomyosin, at higher concentration, is an elastic gel.

G-actin unites with myosin, too, but there is no change in viscosity and no fibres are formed. The G-actomyosin, which is not contractile, will not concern us any longer for

49

the present, and by "actomyosin" I will mean the acto-myosin of F-actin only.

As to the forces which bind actin and myosin to acto-myosin, K. Bailey has shown that SH groups are involved and that there is no actomyosin formation without free SH. F. Guba, studying this question with his quantitative method (blocking the SH by bromoacetophenone) found that myosin, treated with strong urea, contains 4-5 free SH groups per UW. (It contains 6 S altogether). Only one of these is free in native myosin and disappears (does not react any more with the bromoacetophenone) if acto-myosin is formed, to reappear again if the actomyosin is brought to dissociation. If it is blocked, no actomyosin is formed. If the MW of myosin is 1.5×10^6 g., this means that every myosin-particle reacts with about 85 SH groups. Since every such myosin particle is linked, in muscle, to about 8 actin globules, this means 10 SH bridges per actin-globule of MW 76,000 g. This is a very intimate connection. The intimacy of this link finds expression also in the UV spectrum. As found by Gerendás and Szarvas the UV spectrum of actin plus myosin is different from the actomyosin formed from them. We do not know which group of the actin particle is involved in establish-ing these SH bridges. No oxidation is involved in this reaction and there can be no S-S bridges, especially since the SH-s of actin are not involved. The S-S link would be too stable any way.

The adsorption power of myosin is not materially changed by its union with actin, so that we can more or less predict what will happen at different salt concentra-tions. In the complete absence of salts actomyosin is ex-ceedingly hydrophilic and its gel swells in water to a very loose, glassy mass. On addition of very small amounts of KCl (0.001 M) this jelly becomes turbid and begins to shrink. If actomyosin is present in suspension, the sus-pension begins to precipitate. Maximum shrinkage or precipitation is reached at about 0.05 M KCl. If the salt concentration is further increased the protein redissolves. At 0.4 M it remains in solution. This is shown in a very rough way in Fig. 17 by the lower continuous curve. As the curve shows, above 0.4 M, if the number of adsorbed K and Cl ions and herewith the number of charged points is further increased, the viscosity gradually falls to reach asymptotically at 2 M the additive value of the viscosities of actin and myosin. With about 10 K and Cl ions adsorbed in the secondary zone of myosin, actomyosin dissociates. Dissociation is a matter of charge. Above a certain charge actin and myosin do not unite any longer, or dissociate if united.

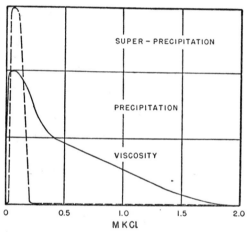

Fig. 17. Semiquantitative curve showing the behavior of actomyosin in the presence (broken line) and absence (solid line) of ATP (0.1%) at varied KCl concentration.

The actomyosin, even at the maximum of precipitation or shrinkage still contains much water. The balance of charges, even at this point, seems to be rather poor, and shrinking and precipitation are moderate. It is hardly possible to obtain a gel or precipitate from actomyosin which contains less than 95% of water.

All this is more or less what might be expected. The

surprise occurs when ATP is added to the system. We might expect that upon the addition of ATP hydration is increased, and precipitation and shrinking inhibited, as was the case with myosin. What actually happens is shown, in a very rough way, by the broken curve in Fig. 17. At low salt concentrations, the complex dissociates completely. At a somewhat higher concentration, the actomyosin is made to precipitate or shrink very rapidly and to dissociate completely again if the salt concentration is somewhat further increased. Reactions are very intense and there is, so to speak, nothing between the two extremes, maximal shrinkage or precipitation, and complete dissociation and dissolution. Actomyosin, in the presence of ATP, either goes to pieces, or if not, it "superprecipitates." We might also say that actomyosin, in the presence of ATP, is stable only within a very narrow range of concentrations, and exists here only in a maximal precipitated or shrunk condition. In the presence of ATP the critical charge, necessary to cause complete dissociation and dissolution, is reached suddenly, but if it is not reached, ATP will have the contrary effect and will cause complete discharge and herewith maximal precipitation or shrinkage.

The decrease in viscosity and DRF, discovered by J. Needham and his associates in "myosin" solution on addition of ATP was evidently due to the dissociation of the actomyosin present.

A few words may be said about this maximal precipitation and shrinkage. Actomyosin, precipitated by the sole action of salts, is very loose, floccular and includes a very great amount of water. In the presence of ATP a granular precipitate is obtained which settles rapidly to the bottom of the tube and occupies a small volume. Even more striking is the shrinking. If the actomyosin is brought into the form of threads (Fig. 3) and is given a big surface, on addition of ATP the shrinkage will be so fast and excessive that it gives the impression of active contraction. To distinguish this excessive shrinking from the slow and moderate shrinking caused by salts alone, I will call it "contraction." The measurement of these contracted threads shows that they cannot contain more than 50% of water. A closer packing than this is hardly possible so that we can say that the contracted threads are composed of anhydrous matter with a little entrapped water.

What is unexpected is not the dissociating effect of ATP which could, more or less, be expected although its intensity is surprising. The surprise is the contraction or superprecipitation. Why should ATP, which has no effect on actin and has a hydrating effect only on myosin cause such a complete discharge? As the analysis shows, the contracted actomyosin contains approximately the same amount of ions adsorbed as free myosin does under the same conditions. It must also contain the equivalent quantity of anions, mostly ATP. If there is a discharge, it can only be due to a more perfect inner balancing of charges within the particles which only takes place in the presence of actin.

Naturally, it is no more than a way of speaking if we say that "ATP makes actomyosin contract." We have a system before us composed of actin, myosin, ATP, K and Mg ions and the system will result in contracted actomyosin if it is complete and all its constituents are present in the right proportions. Contraction will appear on addition of any of these substances which is added last and completes the system, whether it is the ATP, K^+, Mg^{++}, actin, or the myosin.

We can collect data and study this system from different angles. J. Godeau has shown that superprecipitation is inhibited by substances which interfere with SH, which observation is explained by K. Bailey's finding that SH is needed for actomyosin-formation. We can study the system from other angles, for instance in its relation to the ATP concentration.

In the presence of 0.5 M KCl, where actomyosin is on the verge of dissociation, very little ATP is needed to make dissociation complete. As found by W. Mommaerts, 1 mole of ATP per 100,000 g. of actomyosin is sufficient. In order to produce contraction much higher concentrations of ATP are needed. Contraction becomes maximal in the presence of 0.1% ATP where, approximately, 1 ATP molecule is adsorbed per UW of myosin, the same quantity as we find in living muscle. If the concentration of ATP decreases below 0.01% and less than 1 ATP is adsorbed per 76,000 g. no contraction is obtained at all. It follows that with increasing ATP-concentration (which lends increasing charge to the particles) the zone of KCl-concentrations, where contraction (and not dissociation) is obtained, becomes narrower; with decreasing ATP concentration it becomes wider. Thus decreasing ATP concentration favors contraction, increasing ATP concentration favors relaxation. Mg^{++}, which enhances ATP adsorption, further narrows the zone of KCl concentration at which contraction is obtained but strongly promotes contraction within this zone. All these reactions are completely reversible. ATP is essential for both contraction and relaxation.

Another simple question we can study is that of temperature relations. The experiment shows that actin unites with myosin to form actomyosin at any temperature, but that contraction or superprecipitation does not take place at $0°C$. As we raise the temperature the actomyosin gradually superprecipitates to dissolve again as the temperature is lowered to $0°C$. This shows that contraction is an equilibrium-reaction dependent on temperature. If, at a certain medium temperature, the actomyosin contracts only half-way, then the phenomenon may be explained in two ways: either by supposing that the micells are half contracted, or by supposing that only half of the micells contracted. Fig. 17 with its sudden transitions suggests that the latter explanation is the correct one and that the contracted state and the relaxed state are two distinct states and a single particle is either in the one or in the other and there is nothing in between. This rather important assumption is borne out by experiments to be reported later. The formation of a contracted actomyosin from its elements thus takes place in two steps: the actin, myosin and ATP unite to form uncontracted (relaxed) actomyosin, which, in this uncontracted state is stable at a low temperature only. In the second step, at room temperature, the micells go over into their contracted state, the number of micells going over into this state, the equilibrium constant of the two states depending on the temperature.

Since the actin and myosin are both soluble in KCl above 0.1 M, when the actomyosin is brought to dissociation, it dissolves. If it is rendered insoluble by the presence of Mg^{++} which makes actin and myosin more insoluble, the actomyosin may dissociate and hydrate without dissolution. "Relaxed" actomyosin, at 0°C, may be either dissociated or uncontracted actomyosin; at room temperature it can only be dissociated if free ATP is present.

Another simple question is the quantitative relation of actin to myosin. Actomyosin is not a stoichiometric compound and actin will unite with myosin in any proportion, the physical constants of the different myosins being somewhat different. Erdös has found that the contractility of actomyosin was, within limits, independent of the actin-myosin ratio and was maximal in actomyosin containing 2.5-15 parts of myosin to 1 part of actin. The drop in viscosity of an actomyosin solution in 0.5 M KCl on addition of ATP depends, however, very greatly on the actin-myosin ratio and is the greatest if the two are present in the relation of 1:2.5. This is remarkable because Balenovic and Straub found that muscle contains the two proteins in this relation. Although actomyosin is not a stoichiometric compound, this relation of 1:2.5 (which means approximately fifty actin globules to one myosin particle) seems to be more than a fortuitous relation. It was found that 5 parts of myosin were capable of protecting 1 part of actin from destruction by alkali. The relation 1:5, *i.e.*, one myosin molecule to one hundred globules also seems to mean a definite relation.

Another point we can study is ionic concentrations, though we must bear in mind that conditions are very complex and difficult to interpret. We will have three important factors coming into the picture: the forces linking actin to actin-particle, the forces linking actin to myosin, and the forces linking ATP to myosin, which all depend on ions. The situation was recently further complicated by F. B. Straub who found that muscle contains a low-molecular organic compound which inhibits dissociation of actomyosin.

Bearing all these complications in mind we may study the influence of different ions on contraction. Contraction in pure KCl is rather sluggish. If a small amount (0.001 M) of Mg^{++} is added the contraction is greatly enhanced. Rózsa found that this strong enhancing effect is specific for Mg^{++} within its group containing Be^{++}, Ca^{++}, Sr^{++} and Ba^{++}. Ca^{++}, in itself, inhibits contraction. The inhibition can be relieved by Mg^{++} without removing the Ca^{++}. Cu^{++} has a rather involved effect. Added in very small concentrations, it is strongly bound and accumulated by actomyosin and changes entirely the physical properties of actomyosin. The actomyosin loses all contractility completely and becomes very elastic. An actomyosin thread cannot be stretched more than 15% without breaking. In the presence of Cu^{++} it can be stretched 300% becoming doubly refracting. This extension is elastic but if the actomyosin is kept in this stretched condition, it "sets." The Cu^{++} develops its action in three steps. In the first, Cu^{++} is simply bound. In this stage original physical properties and contractility can be restored by washing out the Cu^{++} with dilute cyanide. In the second stage the Cu^{++} oxidizes the SH groups of the protein. In this stage original properties can be restored only if, in addition to the removal of Cu^{++}, the protein is reduced again, either by cysteine or by a higher concentration of cyanide. If the Cu^{++} is allowed to act further irreversible denaturation of the protein sets in.

Geometry of Contraction

As has been shown, contraction is only an extreme degree of shrinkage of a gel. Shrinkage of a gel is a common occurrence in colloidal chemistry, caused mostly by discharge of particles. The fact that the contracting matter is built of two proteins indicates that the shrinking or contraction has its special geometry.

At first sight, there is one marked difference between the contraction of muscle fibers and the contraction of our actomyosin threads. Contraction of muscle is anisodiametric: muscle does not shrink in all directions. It becomes shorter and at the same time wider. In fact, muscle does not shrink at all in the classical sense, its volume remaining constant. Our thread shrinks, and shrinks isodiametrically, becoming shorter and thinner at the same time (Fig. 3). Corresponding to this there is also a marked difference between the structure of muscle fibres and actomyosin threads: while in the former the actomyosin filaments run coaxially to the fibre, they are distributed at random in the latter. Gerendás, however, has shown that it is possible to arrange the filaments parallel to the axis in threads too, and that is by stretching them. In order to do so he had to compromise.

57

Native threads are contractile but cannot be stretched; metal-denatured threads can be stretched but do not contract. Gerendás succeeded by *partly* denaturing the thread by means of a light metal, like Zn. By this treatment the threads became extensible up to 200% and retained some of their contractility. Such a thread, if made to contract with ATP, contracted aniso-diametrically, becoming shorter and thicker, like muscle. For example, a thread, treated with 0.001 M Zn SO_4, could be stretched 200%, becoming thereby double-re-fracting (12.10^{-4}) which indicates an orientation of the micells parallel to the axis. On addition of ATP the thread shortened by 30%, and became wider by 55%, contracted thus anisodiametrically like muscle, keeping its volume constant.

This observation is rather important, not only because it brings actomyosin in line with muscle, but also because it gives us some information about the mechanism of con-traction. Extensive shrinking of colloids is due to the loss of intermicellar water. If, in our stretched thread, the actomyosin micells are parallel to the fibre axis, then evidently, the intermicellar spaces are parallel to it also. But if these spaces filled with water are parallel to the axis, then the expulsion of this intermicellar water could never make the fibre shorter; it could only make it thinner which is the opposite of what happens.

This can be explained only by assuming that the micells themselves have become shorter. W. T. Astbury sup-poses that in contraction the polypeptide chains of myosin become shorter by folding up. This may be so, but once having been shown that the contractile sub-stance is built of two protins, the question cannot be dismissed in this simple way and there must be a more complex geometry involved.

So far the EM has shown that actin forms long threads and the elongated myosin-rodlets attach themselves length-

wise to the actin-thread. We have seen that free myosin is
easily discharged by ions and undergoes marked changes
in hydration under their influence, while actin is quite
inert in this respect. If these qualities are maintained in
actomyosin then we have here an elongated system built
of two partners with different capacities of shrinking. If,
in such a system, one of the partners shrinks or expands
more than the other the whole system has to bend. A
relatively small difference in the hydration of the two
components will cause a relatively strong bending and
herewith a shortening of the whole system. This is shown,
very schematically, in Fig. 18. If black (myosin) shrinks,
the whole system has to curl up (and shorten by 2/3),

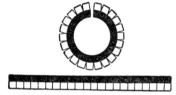

Fig. 18. Schematized model of relaxed and contracted actomyosin particle.

provided the other partner (actin) can break up into
smaller particles (as it actually does). The bending of
such systems is well known to physicists (bimetallic strips)
and housewives (bending of wooden boards, caused by
humidity).

Such a theory would solve an old puzzle: great changes
in dimensions of colloids are produced by long-distance
forces which are weak and unfit to do work. Short-distance
forces may do work but will entail only small changes in
dimensions. In muscular contraction changes in dimensions are extensive and work is done throughout. In the
above mechanism short-distance-forces, due to slight
shrinking of myosin, would be magnified to extensive

59

motion by bending. This bending would have to take place in molecular dimensions within a spiral structure. My pre-EM-theory, which places bending into microscopic dimensions, is certainly incorrect. But there is no point in speculating about this problem any more until the splendid possibilities, offered by the EM, are exhausted. The possibility, however, that muscular contraction is not due to bending of peptide chains within the myosin-particle but to the bending of the whole particle should not be left out of consideration. As mentioned, Dr. G. Rózsa has found indications of a spiral structure in actin as well as in actomyosin.

The fact that contracted muscle still shows the x-ray pattern of stretched polypeptide chains does not rule out the possibility of bending of particles unless such pictures are not taken from muscle in which all actomyosin particles are certainly present in contracted state. If the contraction of the single particles is an all-or-none reaction and if the bent particles give no x-ray pattern at all, contracted muscle must give the pattern of stretched chains until all its micells are contracted.

Energy-Relations

Another question of basic importance is the question of energetics. What are the energy changes during contraction? If the splitting of ATP is the source of the energy of muscular contraction, we are unable to fit this process into its proper place until we know why the muscle needs energy at all. I mean to say, until we know whether muscle needs energy for its contraction or its relaxation. Common sense would demand energy for contraction, but as has been pointed out by Ritchie long ago, muscle might just as well work as a stretched rubber band which uses its own inner energy for its contraction, and needs a supply of energy from without for its distending or relaxation. To put it plainly: muscle may release energy first and do its work later, or may do its work first and do the release later. This latter possibility has been termed by von Muralt in a somewhat picturesque way the "watercloset theory."

As has been shown before, the process of contraction is an equilibrium reaction depending on temperature. If this is so, then the situation becomes rather interesting, for the dependence of the equilibrium constant on temperature permits us to calculate changes in energy. Our first step must be to find the equilibrium constant at different temperatures.

I have mentioned before that there are reasons to believe that the contracted and the relaxed state of the single actomyosin particle are two distinct states with no inbetween: it's either Jack or Jill. If this is correct then we can easily calculate the equilibrium constant from the length of an actomyosin thread. In this case maximum contraction means that 100% of the micells is contracted and complete relaxation means that 0% is contracted. Contraction to the half-way point means that half of the micells is contracted and the equilibrium constant is $1/1$ etc. We would therefore simply have to measure the length of a thread in the presence of ATP and the necessary ions at various temperatures. We would obtain the equilibrium constants for different temperatures or at any rate we would obtain some sort of a number. Now, if our theory is correct and contraction and relaxation are distinct states of matter at equilibrium, then we must expect that the natural logarithm of these numbers, if plotted against the reciprocal value of the absolute temperature, will give a straight line.

These experiments have been performed by L. Varga. As "actomyosin-thread" he used muscle in the first instance. The psoas of the rabbit was washed in water at $0°C.$, for several days. Then it was cut into slices on the freezing-microtome, each slice containing one sheet of parallel running muscle fibres. Then the fibres were made to contract at different temperatures by adding ATP and the necessary ions and the final length measured.* (Fig. 19).

The natural logarithm of the equilibrium constants, obtained this way, plotted against 1/T is reproduced for the frog and the rabbit in Fig. 20. It is a perfectly straight line proving that our theories were correct and contraction of actomyosin micells is an all-or-none reaction. If this had not been so, some other curve would have been obtained.

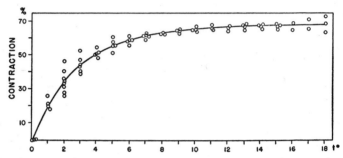

Fig. 19.   Contraction of muscle slices at varied temperatures in the presence of KCl and ATP.

Having estimated the temperature constants for different temperatures it is easy to calculate energy changes by means of van't Hoff's equations. The calculation shows that contraction is endothermic, actomyosin taking up 56,000 cal. from its surroundings. At the same time the free energy of the system drops. It follows that contraction is a spontaneous process, that the contracted actomyosin is the more stable, energy-poorer modification and the system uses its own inner energy. At the same time the system cools down somewhat. From this we can deduce a

*The muscle rapidly contracts in a few minutes to reach its final length asymptotically. If the muscle is now stored for a very long time, e.g., over night, it will be found to have contracted further. This second contraction is of a different nature and is probably due to the secondary cohesion of the particles. Such cohesions between contracted actomyosin particles are easily developed and eventually, any muscle must be found at any temperature in contracted state.

very important consequence: the supply of free energy from without is needed for relaxation.

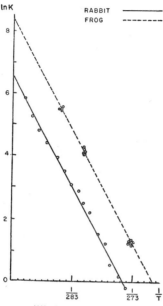

Fig. 20. ln of the equilibrium-constant of actomyosin contraction plotted against l/T. Broken line: frog; full line: rabbit.

The drop of free energy of the system depends on temperature. At 37°C. it is 7000 cal. for the rabbit. This amount of energy, at least, must therefore be imparted to the system if we want it to relax isothermally at constant ionic concentrations. The total energy of the pyrophosphate-bond of ATP is 11,000 cal. and Meyerhof showed that its free energy is about equal to this. The splitting of one phosphate-link will thus suffice to bring the system back to relaxation.*

It is a matter of interesting speculation whether the process may be considered as isothermal. If relaxation follows contraction within thousandths of a second, the mole-

*More correctly the $\triangle$ F of actomyosin in contraction is 7-8000 cal while the $\triangle$ F of ATP is 11,000-12,000 cal.

cule might have no chance to take up heat from the surrounding fluid and might thus be "cool" and need less free energy for relaxation.

The free energy changes in the rabbit in their dependence on temperature are reproduced in the lower curve of Fig. 21. As will be seen the curve cuts the abscissa just above 0°C. which explains why rabbit's muscle is unable to contract at this temperature.

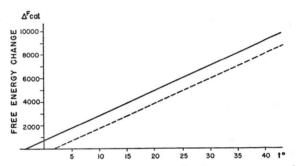

Fig. 21.   Free energy change in muscle slices on contraction at varied temperatures. Upper curve: frog; lower (broken curve): rabbit.

It was a rather unpleasant surprise one day to find a frog swimming in ice water at 0°C. after these experiments had been concluded. We had to find out whether the frog or Dr. Varga was wrong. The experiments were repeated with frog-muscle and gave a somewhat higher curve, still allowing for a small drop of free energy at 0°C., and herewith limited motion, thus allowing the frog to swim in ice water as he has to do sometimes. The curve cuts the abscissa at −3°C. Here the frog will be unable to swim but this temperature does not interest him anymore, because he is frozen anyway. So it seems, both Dr. Varga and the frog were correct (Fig. 21).

These experiments were repeated with actomyosin threads which gave almost identical curves with muscle. This is rather important because it shows that both processes, contraction of muscle and contraction of actomyosin are, in essence, identical processes.

Dr. Varga's measurements on actomyosin are important for another reason. There is one difficulty with our calculations of energy. They all relate to the molar quantity. To the molar quantity of what? The contractile filaments are continuous structures and have no molar quantity. Actomyosin threads are of different length and have no molar quantity. The identity of the curves of muscle and actomyosin shows that the calculation must relate to a definite unit; definite units of actin, of myosin, or of atomyosin. In muscle we are unable to vary the relative quantities of these substances; in actomyosin threads we can. Actin, having a much smaller MW than myosin, the variation of its quantity in actomyosin would have to alter the course of our curves to a great extent. The experiment showed that the variation of the actin content did not matter and the results depended only on the molar quantity of myosin present. The molar quantity, in this case, is not that of the colloidal myosin particle of MW $1\text{-}1.5 \times 10^6$ g. but a sub-unit thereof, possibly that of MW 76,000 g. It is this quantity which needs 7000 cal., *i.e.,* the splitting of one phosphate for its relaxation.

In resting muscle about 70 ATP molecules are adsorbed to every myosin particle. As has been indicated and will be shown later, this entire quantity of ATP is needed to keep the muscle in maximally reactive form, to contract or relax maximally. Only part of these 70 ATP molecules will be called upon to sacrifice itself for the community. These will have to be in a special position in which they will be capable of reacting with the myosin in some way chemically. We know what this point must be: the ATP-P-protin, linked to the skeleton (Fig. 10). The protin only will be able to deal with the ATP molecule chemically and split its pyrophosphate link. If the supply of labile phosphate and herewith the recovery of ATP is cut off, the muscle may be expected still to make a number of contractions. But by and by the relaxation must suffer and become more and more incomplete as the ATP becomes exhausted, relaxation needing more adsorbed ATP than contraction. This is actually what we see in monoiodoacetic acid poisoning where the supply of energy-rich phosphate is cut off and where the muscle is still capable of several contractions finishing up its career in contracture.

Creatine phosphate has no specific action on the physical properties of actomyosin and there seems to be no direct relation whatever between the two. The store of this high-energy phosphate is needed to re-phosphorylate any ADP and keep, in this way, the concentration of ATP constant. The phosphate of creatine is replaced by fermentation (and oxidation ?). In this way creatine phosphate serves as a link between energy production and energy consumption. This PO_4 transport could not be effected by ATP since there can be no free ATP in muscle.

The $\triangle$ F curves of Dr. Varga involve another very fascinating implication. They tell us that if the temperature goes up to 53 °C. the $\triangle F$ of actomyosin reaches 11,000 cal and the energy of ATP must become insufficient for relaxation and the muscle must go into contracture. This is what actually happens giving a very simple explanation of the mechanism of the heat contracture which occupied so much of the attention of earlier physiologists. At about 45° the rabbit's muscle begins to develop contracture which, with increasing temperature becomes stronger to reach the maximum sharply at 53°. One can almost titrate in this way the free energy of ATP with the help of Varga's curve. In the frog maximal contracture is reached a few degrees lower corresponding to the somewhat higher $\triangle F$ curve. These curves also indicate that the free energy of ATP is transferred onto actomyosin without loss.

That heat contracture is not simply a rough colloidal change due to the heat denaturation of the protein may easily be shown by the fact that the muscle of the rabbit, after having lost its ATP and excitability on a few hours storage, gives no heat contracture at these low temperatures.

In the light of these results 11,000 cal. seem rather a waste for animals which constantly live at a relatively low temperature, as do crustaceans living at the bottom of the sea. The unit of energy seems to be here 8000 cal. instead of 11,000, as indicated by the energy of arginine phosphate (Meyerhof) which takes the place of creatine phosphate in these animals.

Dr. Varga has lately completed his experiments by also measuring the rate of contraction, *i.e.,* the rate of transition of relaxed into contracted actomyosin at different temperatures. The transition follows the monomolecular type of reaction. The dependence of the reaction constant on temperature allows the calculation of the activation energy of the process which is 20,000 cal.

Energy Production and Energy Consumption

One of the most basic problems of general physiology is: What regulates the liberation of energy? When I was a student and was asked this question on an examination I had to answer that together with the impulse for action there was an impulse for energy liberation coming along. In other words, when the central nervous system wired to the muscle "contract," it added to the message: "I am sending you through the same mail a cheque for so many calories to cover your expenses."

After thirty years of acquaintance with Nature I would be quite disappointed if Nature could not think of a better mechanism. After all, all life revolves around energy and we can expect that the process of its liberation is most carefully regulated, regulated automatically with a great precision to avoid waste as much as possible.

This question cannot be solved by studying free myosin which is an enzyme "turned loose," liberated from its natural inhibitions, taken out from the mechanism in which it has to fit. Free myosin means a lower degree of organization than we find in actomyosin. Not even extracted actomyosin will do and we must take whole muscle, thus actomyosin fitted into its mechanism at the level of organization at which it performs its basic biological function.

The approach to this problem was opened by a rather unexpected observation of A. Biró and A. E. Szent-Györgyi who found that the temperature coefficient of the phosphatase activity of myosin is rather low. We are accustomed to see enzymatic reactions increase their rate 2.5-3 times if we raise the temperature by 10°C. The ATP-ase activity of myosin increased but by a factor of about 1.4. This is important because contraction has a very high temperature coefficient. As I have shown before, at 0°C. there is no contraction at all, while at 16°C. contraction is maximal. Now if both processes, contraction and ATP-ase activity, would have an equally high coefficient, it would be difficult to say what is due to the elevation of temperature as such and what to contraction. The great difference of coefficient permits us to distinguish between the two processes.

Conditions are not quite simple and I have to stop at this point for a moment. Contraction and enzymic activity both depend on charge and charge depends on concentration, *vis.*, adsorption of ions. The physiological ionic concentration, corresponding to that of serum or Ringer, marks a critical point. Below this concentration the actomyosin or muscle fibre splits ATP whether contracted or not and splits it the more intensely the further we go below the physiological concentration. This unphysiological range will not interest us further. What is of interest is that at the physiological ionic concentration (or above), muscle, at 0°C., is not contracted and does not split ATP. As we raise the temperature above 0°C.

the muscle starts to contract and to split ATP. The contraction has in the beginning a very high temperature quotient which falls off at the measure as we approach $16°C$. where contraction becomes maximal. The splitting of ATP in this range, follows the high temperature quotient of contraction and falls to 1.4 at the measure as we approach $16°C$. This means that the enzymic activity does not depend on temperature as such, but depends on contraction and only contracted actomyosin is enzymatically active.

This result may seem strange at first but appears natural on closer consideration. Contraction and inner discharge of the particle are one and the same process, which lowers the charge below the critical level at or above which actomyosin is enzymatically inactive.

Biro and A. E. Szent-Györgyi have shown that these observations hold true both for muscle and isolated actomyosin but not for free myosin. Free myosin has no two physical states as has actomyosin. This latter is only active as phosphatase in its low-energy, discharged, contracted form when it needs energy for its relaxation.

This gives us a most satisfactory explanation of the way Nature regulates energy liberation. The relaxed actomyosin in its high-energy state needs no energy and it is not an enzyme; at least not an ATP-ase which splits pyrophosphate-bonds. Going over into its lower energy-state it becomes enzymatically active and splits ATP, one ATP molecule per unit of myosin and returns with the energy thus liberated, into its inactive high-energy state where it is no longer an enzyme. It is thus the need of energy which entails its liberation, and which sees to it that no more ATP molecules should be split than necessary. Higher organization means not only wider scope, it means limitations just as well. Whole life seems to be based on a limitation: it performs exergic reactions in mechanisms which do not allow the energy produced to turn into heat. The idea, expressed before, "need of energy limiting energy production" could perhaps be expressed also by saying that the living structure is capable of performing exergic reactions when it knows where to put the energy liberated. Myosin, in free condition, taken out from the higher pattern, will split ATP freely, without rhyme or reason, converting its energy into heat.

It seemed interesting to know whether this principle also applies to other processes, like that of oxidation. We have little information about the relation of oxidation to contraction and do not know whether oxidative energy is used at all for relaxation or whether oxidation is used in this respect only to make high-energy phosphate bonds. The work of Ochoa has shown that certain oxidations, like that of succinic acid, are rather effective in producing high-energy phosphate links.

We have every reason to suppose that in other, more slowly and evenly working organs like the brain or kidney, oxidative energy is used directly for function. If oxidation is arrested, as by cyanide or lack of O_2, function stops immediately. These organs contain very little ATP (if any). Muscle contains great amounts of ATP and with it a great store of energy and is able to work for quite a long period of time without oxidation or even without pyrophosphate coming from outside. Professor Lundsgaard was good enough to inform me that a muscle in moniodoacetate poisoning, with fermentation cut off, is still capable of 70 full contractions which may be connected with the number of ATP molecules adsorbed to a myosin particle in normal muscle, which is just about 70.*

Naturally, this is no evidence that muscle does not use oxidative energy for its function. If other organs do so we may expect the same to be true for muscle even if

*This very close agreement is evidently a coincidence for creatine-phosphate is there too and muscle is not contractile below a certain ATP saturation.

oxidation could not cover the very sudden and large needs in muscle.

To come to the point, many years ago I showed that the main furnace in the muscle cell is succinoxidase and the H's of the foodstuffs are transferred on to this substance and the greatest part of oxidative energy is liberated by oxidizing the H's of succinate and releasing the excess energy of its electrons. This system of succinic oxidation is a rather complex one. The succinic dehydogenase of Thunberg lends a high escaping tendency to the electrons of succinate and the electrons are transferred over a series of cytochromes on to oxygen which is its final acceptor. The oxygen is activated for this reaction by the cytochrome-oxidase. At every step of this chain the electron loses part of its energy till it reaches its minimum by being coupled to oxygen.

Later, this picture was completed by A. Krebs by bringing citric acid into the picture which does not change anything of the principle to be discussed here, the citricodehydrogenase having qualities very similar to those of the succinodehydrogenase.

A. Biró and A. E. Szent-Györgyi asked themselves whether this succinic oxidation had anything to do with contraction. They found that their muscle was most active as succinoxidase under conditions in which it was maximally contracted while it was inactive under conditions in which it was relaxed. Further analysis of this phenomenon showed that it is neither the dehydrogenase, nor the oxygen activation which depends upon contraction. It seems that the bridge between the two, the electron transport is broken in relaxation when the muscle needs no energy. Muscle may thus contain in its relaxed state both active oxygen and active hydrogen, with the two being unable to react with one another.

It is possible that in oxidation we meet the same principle: regulation of energy liberation by the need of energy, the system being active only when in its low energy contracted state and needing energy for its relaxation.

There might be even a fluid equilibrium between oxidation, phosphate-breakdown or the building of it and the energy-state of muscle. Put into other words this would mean that the equilibrium-constant of the reaction of phosphate-splitting⇄phosphate-synthesis is different for relaxed and contracted actomyosin, being shifted in the sense of the upper arrow for relaxed, in the sense of the lower arrow for contracted actomyosin. If we assume that the excess energy of electrons serves to charge up actomyosin and that phosphate-splitting produces, while phosphate-synthesis uses up such excess energy; so contraction and relaxation, fermentation and oxidation, fat, carbohydrate and phosphate, all come together into one single and simple picture. Whether this picture represents the truth is another question.*

*If the above picture is correct, there must be a different oxidation system for lactic acid, for oxidizing lactate to pyruvate, which oxidation takes place in relaxation, in the recovery period. The co-dehydrogenase is involved in this system.

FOURTH LECTURE

THE MUSCLE FIBRE

General Remarks

In my previous lectures I took you through different levels of organization. We worked our way from actin globules to actin-threads, from protin and myosin skeleton to the complete myosin-particle, then from actin and myosin to the actomyosin-filament. The highest level I can take you to on this occasion is the muscle fibre. Let us follow the contractile matter to this level and see whether our experience brings us any closer to the understanding of muscular contraction.

Our first question may be whether the colloidal phenomena observed, shrinking, superprecipitation, contraction, swelling or dissociation of actomyosin have anything at all to do with muscular contraction. This question can, I think, definitely be answered in the affirmative. We have progressed step by step from actin and myosin to muscle. We have shown that superprecipitation and shrinking of actomyosin are produced in a specific way by ATP and ions, at concentrations at which these substances are all present in muscle. We have shown that this shrinking of actomyosin, if produced in an actomyosin thread, with micells arranged, shows the characteristic feature of muscular contraction: anisodiametric shortening without change in volume. Then we proceeded to show that the same response could be elicited by the same substances in washed and frozen muscle fibres in which the subtler regulations and mechanisms were destroyed and only the actomyosin was preserved. From

73

here on there is but one step to the whole muscle fibre. We have also seen that physical constants (activation energy, equilibrium and reaction constants) are identical in actomyosin and muscle fibres; we could even predict heat-contracture of the living muscle fibre from our data obtained on actomyosin.

Our next question might be whether conditions in our actomyosin-threads are identical with conditions in the muscle-fibre. This question can be answered with an equally definite "no." There are many important differences between the two structures. To start with, the whole inner structure is different: the muscle fibre contains its actin in the form of continuous threads, reaching, perhaps, from one end of the muscle to the other. Consequently the actomyosin filaments are endless too. In isolated, especially reprecipitated actomyosin this structure is broken up into small fragments. These fragments are oriented at random, or if oriented by stretching they are oriented at the expense of deformation. In the fibre these filaments are running nicely parallel to the fibre-axis. Actomyosin, prepared directly from muscle, also contains an excess of myosin, may thus contain free myosin which is hydrated only by ATP and may act, so to speak, as a lubricant for the slipping of actomyosin filaments. So we must be especially careful when trying to draw conclusions from mechanical properties of actomyosin, as for example, its tensile strength, elasticity modulus, slipping etc., on muscle fibres and must not draw the conclusion that threads are useless if results, on this line, show differences with muscle.

There are important differences between actomyosin threads and muscle fibres not only in regard to the contractile matter but also in regard to intermicellar spaces. Thread contains approximately 2% solid matter and 98% water. The quantity of water is thus very great as compared with the quantity of solid matter. In the muscle fibril we find approximately 20% solid matter and 80% water, part of which must be bound to the protein and is not free. The relation of protein to water is therefore much higher in the muscle-fibres than in the actomyosin threads which are mostly suspended in a relatively large volume of water, in comparison with which the volume of the thread is negligible. In the case of threads the adsorption of dissolved substances to actomyosin will not appreciably diminish their concentration in the fluid, but in the muscle-fibre the concentration of dissolved substances will be determined more or less by this adsorption. Let us calculate for a moment. According to Hill and Kupalow the total concentration of Ca^{++} in the muscle is 0.007 M, and according to Dubuisson 0.006 M. 2.5% actin is roughly 0.002 M calculated for the UW. If every UW of actin binds one Ca ion, this leaves us with 0.005 M Ca^{++} in solution. Myosin also strongly binds one Ca^{++} per UW, and the concentration of myosin in 0.005 M. This would leave us with no Ca^{++} at all, or at least with very little free Ca^{++} which is in equilibrium with the adsorbed Ca^{++}.

The situation is somewhat simpler with Mg^{++}, which is present in higher total concentration, 0.014 M according to Hill and Kupalow, and 0.012 M according to Dubuisson. If actin adsorbs one Mg^{++} per UW, this leaves us with about 0.01 M Mg^{++} in solution. In the presence of 0.01 M $MgCl_2$ myosin binds 3 equivalents per UW. This makes 0.0075 M leaving us with 0.0025 M of free Mg^{++}.

The case of K^+ is the simplest of the three. Muscle contains about 0.1 M K^+ and actin has a very low affinity for this ion and the quantities adsorbed to this protein will therefore not modify the total concentration appreciably. Myosin at this concentration would adsorb two ions per UW, *i.e.,* 0.01 M, which would leave us with 0.09 M. As mentioned before, myosin seems to be unable to distinguish between K^+ and Na^+ and so, for simplicity we may pull the two together on first approximation. Muscle contains about 0.04 M Na,+ making the total K+ Na++ concentration 0.14 M. Muscle containing 20% solid matter and only 80% water, has an actual concentration of approximately 0.17 M. Since some of the water is not free, the actual concentration must still be higher. Myosin at this concentration will adsorb 3 ions per UW, which makes 0.015 M all told, and this leaves us with about 0.16 M free K+ Na+. Muscle is isotonic with a 0.16 M NaCl solution and I want you to keep this value of 0.16 well in mind for the rest of our discussion.

The compound for which these considerations are especially important is ATP. The total concentration of ATP in fresh, resting muscle is 0.25 mg. per g., *i.e.,* 0.005 M. At the ionic concentrations in muscle the 0.005 M of myosin present will easily bind one molecule of ATP per UW, thus binding the whole of it.* As I have shown before, myosin can be expected to bind 3 alkali metal ions in muscle in its secondary sphere which is just equivalent to the charge of one ATP molecule. The system is thus well balanced and the ATP bound very strongly and we can expect to find practically no free ATP in muscle. But we may also expect that the fixation of ATP will become weaker and ATP might be released if, for some reason or other, adsorbed K or Na ions are released, either through a dilution of the medium, or under the influence of an electric field. Should the Mg++ or Ca++, adsorbed in the primary zone, be detached, then most of the ATP would have to be released, but resting muscle can contain no free ATP.

These considerations make it probable that in muscle

*A small quantity of ATP must also be bound by the enzymes of fermentation which phosphorylate ATP. The link between the sites of fermentation and myosin, *i.e.,* the sites of phosphorylation and dephosphorylation is made by creatine phosphate. There are enzymes in muscle, the phosphorpherases, studied by Lohman and later in more detail by I. Banga, which readily load over the phosphate of ATP on to creatine at the sites of its formation and from creatine on to adenosine di- or monophosphate on myosin, at the sites of dephosphorylation.

the myosin is in a relation to ATP which cannot be duplicated *in vitro*. *In vivo* the myosin skeleton is well saturated with ATP while its protins are probably free of this nucleotide. *In vitro* this condition cannot be imitated, for if we want to saturate the skeleton with ATP we must employ the nucleotide in excess, leaving relatively great amounts of it free in the fluid. As a result the protin, too, will freely bind ATP. As will be shown later, there are reasons to believe, that ATP molecules, attaching themselves to the protin, have a decisive influence on the physical state of the whole actomyosin particle inducing its discharge.

There is one more important difference between extracted actomyosin, and actomyosin in muscle, which should be mentioned. Extracted actomyosin, in presence of ATP, contracts in KCl up to the concentration of about 0.16 M to dissociate if the salt concentration exceeds this value. 0.16 M means also for the actomyosin, as it is in muscle, a critical concentration, as has been shown already in the discussion of the ATP-ase activity and will be shown in discussing excitation. Something happens at this salt concentration which is analogous to happenings in extracted actomyosin, but the system does not dissolve. It dissolves only above 0.5 M KCl and is capable of contracting up to this concentration. As will be shown this region of salt concentrations of 0.16-0.5 M, is most important for the understanding of muscle. What this difference between extracted actomyosin and actomyosin *in situ* is due to, we do not know. It is possible that in muscle the myosin micells are associated end-to-end, the links being broken up irreversibly by the high charge induced by 0.5 M KCl in presence of ATP during extraction.

Rest

The basic state of muscle is rest. In order to study it let us start by putting freshly isolated muscle fibres into

77

KCl of varying concentration. We have done the same before with our actomyosin threads and the result is summarized in Fig. 17. The top half of Fig. 22 is exactly the same curve as shown in Fig. 17, with the one difference that the KCl concentrations on the abscissa are not on numerical but on logarithmic scale. This broadens the

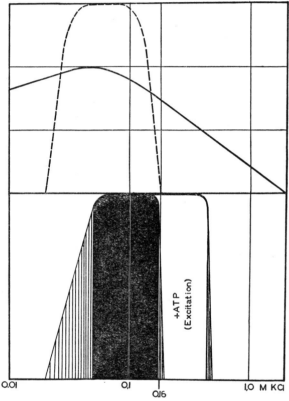

Fig. 22. Behavior of actomyosin thread (upper curve) and muscle fibre (lower curve) in KCl solutions of varied concentration.

curve and makes its discussion somewhat easier. Moreover, I believe, that Nature herself thinks in logarithmic rather than in numerical scales.

In the lower half of Fig. 22 is shown the behavior of a freshly isolated muscle fibre under the same conditions, the only difference being that while there was ATP added to the actomyosin thread (top curve) there was no ATP added to the muscle fibre because freshly isolated muscle fibres contain a rather large quantity of it anyway.

The black area shows the KCl zone in which all fibres contracted maximally. To the left of this area is a rather broad hatched area in which there was partial contraction which, being rather far from physiological concentrations, will not interest us any more. To the right of the black area of full contraction there is a very narrow hatched zone of partial contraction with part of the fibres contracted or fibres partly contracted. The partial contraction within this narrow zone is evidently due to imperfections of the technique and has to be discounted.

On comparing the top and the bottom curves (borrowed from Dr. G. Rózsa) we are struck with the great similarity, almost identity of the two curves.

Now let us tarry for a while at this lower curve. The contractile matter here is composed of actin threads with myosin particles attached to them, myosin particles with 70-85 ATP molecules and three times as many K^{++} Na^+ adsorbed and the basic negative charges neutralized by Mg^{++}. In regard to ATP, and this is what chiefly interests us at the moment, the situation corresponds to Fig. 10, myosin rods well provided with ATP but with proteins free of it.*

Another remarkable feature of this lower curve in Fig. 22 is the relation of the black zone of contraction to the isotonic 0.16 M KCl concentration, marked by a vertical line. The black area is just to the left of it. The isotonic ionic concentration means thus the concentration in which the muscle just does not contract: the isotonic KCl or

*This condition cannot be reproduced in actomyosin threads for there will always be an excess of ATP in solution.

NaCl just lends the critical charge to it which prevents its contraction. As the experiment shows, diluting the isotonic salt solution by no more than 10% of water, suffices to elicit full contraction lowering the charge of myosin below the critical level.

Excitation

Something very unexpected happens if we add ATP to the isotonic or slightly hypertonic (0.2-0.3 M) KCl solution, as Dr. Rózsa has found. We would expect that the addition of ATP makes no difference at all, plenty of ATP having been present already. In spite of this expectation the muscle reacts with a violent contraction on the addition of ATP and contracts up to 0.5 M KCl. The curve has changed. The zone of contraction has been extended to the right as shown in Fig. 22. I believe that this new added area of contraction is the area of excitation. Anyway, we must conclude that the added ATP acts differently from the ATP already present in muscle, extending the curve to the right.

The first thought on making this observation is that the two ATP's, the ATP present and the ATP added are different chemically, but all efforts to demonstrate such a difference have failed and this theory has to be discarded. If it is the same ATP, then the mechanism of action, the localization of the action of the two must be different, and the added free ATP must be able to reach reactive points of myosin which the adsorbed ATP cannot.

That this is actually the case is demonstrated by further observations of Dr. Rózsa, which makes the story still more remarkable. He found that the addition of 0.0005 mg. ATP per ml. was enough to obtain contraction. Now this is remarkable because we have shown that such a small concentration of ATP can never cause contraction of actomyosin at all. A thousand times as much ATP is needed to induce such an energetic contraction. Thus, if 0.0005 mg. does the trick, then it is evident that it was not this small quantity of added ATP which made the actomyosin contract. What made it contract was the large quantity of ATP present and the added ATP only had a trigger action by reacting with a special point of the myosin particle. We can guess with great probability what this point is: the ATP-protin.

According to this picture added ATP produces contraction by reacting with the ATP-protin and by changing in this way the curve of actomyosin, as shown in Fig. 22. This change causes the muscle now to contract at the isotonic salt concentration at which it was unable to contract before. The association of ATP with the protin seems to induce a change in the whole particle which entails the mutual neutralization of the positive and negative charges present. This way the charge is lowered below the critical level and remains there even if we increase the KCl concentration up to 0.45 M. How the ATP does this we do not know. There might be a phosphate transfer from ATP to myosin, but we have no data on this point. Probably some subtler quantum mechanical process is involved.

When Dr. Rózsa made his observations, being cut off from the literature, he was unaware that the trigger action of ATP was already discovered by F. Buchthal and his associates Deutsch and Knappeis who also showed that this action of ATP was not quite specific and was given by different substances containing pyrophosphate, even by inorganic triphosphate. This indicates that in this effect of ATP the pyrophosphate end of the molecule is involved. This brings out even sharper the difference between the two, or rather three different actions of ATP:

1. The trigger action, probably due to the combination of ATP-protin and pyrophosphate. Accordingly, to elicit this reaction, very small quantities of ATP are needed. In Buchtal's experiments the quantity of ATP was small but its concentration rather high. In Rózsa's experiments

both were low and there was less than one molecule of ATP per molecule of myosin if we suppose a diffusion equilibrium between muscle fibre and suspension-fluid.

2. The action of ATP adsorbed to the myosin skeleton, which ATP renders the protein reactive, capable of contraction and relaxation. This ATP also has a decisive influence on the physical state of resting actomyosin keeping it fully relaxed and supple. Relatively large quantities of ATP are needed to keep the muscle in this state which is reached if one ATP molecule is adsorbed per UW of myosin, or 85 molecules of ATP per molecule of myosin (if 1,500,000 g. is taken as MW). This action of myosin is highly specific and is shared by ADP only. This indicates that other parts of the molecule than the pyrophosphate are also involved in this action. Buchthal (oral communication) has actually shown that the UV adsorption-spectrum of ATP, adsorbed to myosin, is different from that of free ATP which indicates not only that the adenine-end of the molecule is involved in the adsorption but indicates also that the link between nucleotide and protein is a very intimate one.

3. The function of ATP as energy-donator. This function involves the splitting of the pyrophosphate link by myosin, *viz.*, its corresponding protin. This splitting induces relaxation.

That the reaction of free ATP with the protin is actually involved in the mechanism of excitation and the added ATP acts by putting in motion the normal apparatus of excitation, is made highly probable by the fact that an unexcitable muscle does not show any such reaction. If we permit the muscle to lose excitability on storage and subject the isolated fibre in this condition to the experiment it will still readily contract on addition of ATP, but only if we add the very high concentrations of ATP which are needed to produce contraction of extracted actomyosin. The small concentrations effective in excitable muscle have now no action whatever. Dr. Rózsa finds that muscle loses excitability if its ATP concentration decreases on storage below half of its physiological level. These observations corroborate Buchthal's view which assigns to ATP an important rôle in excitation. How the pyrophosphate, adsorbed to the protin, starts up the discharge of the myosin particle, and how this reaction is propagated through the whole length of the myosin particle, is at present but the subject of rather delicious speculation.

Contraction

What we called "excitation" in the previous chapter was a change in the actomyosin particle inducing its discharge. Naturally, by this we did not mean a complete neutralization of charges or a change in net charge, but only a shift of these charges which allows more complete mutual neutralization of their fields of forces. Repulsive forces having been eliminated attractions prevail and the mutual approach of particles within the specific geometry causes shortening.

Relaxation

As has been made probable in the previous lectures, discharge and the consecutive contraction of the actomyosin-particle are elicited by an ATP-molecule, attaching itself to the ATP-protin. The particle, by its discharge and contraction, becomes enzymatically active and decomposes this ATP splitting its high-energy phosphate bond. In this way the energy, necessary for relaxation, is liberated and at the same time the myosin particle gets rid of the ATP molecule which caused its discharge.

This suggests that the process of relaxation itself, the transition of the contracted energy-poor actomyosin into the relaxed energy-rich form is simply the reversal of the contraction process, the particle simply stretching out again after the necessary energy has been imparted to it and caused its being re-charged. There are, however, indications that the story is more involved than this.

As mentioned before, only the actomyosin, formed from fibrous actin and myosin, is contractile. If such an actomyosin is made to contract by ATP and is suddenly dissolved we find the actin in globular form: the threads have broken up to globules, probably under some tension developed in contraction as indicated schematically in Fig. 18. The actomyosin, containing globular actin, is quite different from actomyosin containing fibrous actin; the former has a low viscosity and is not contractile at all. As Fig. 18 shows all this will have no special effect as long as the system is in its contracted anhydrous low energy state.

However, as soon as the energy of ATP is communicated to the myosin particle and this goes back to its hydrated high energy state, the myosin and the globular actin will dissociate, because globular actin does not form a compound with myosin if the latter has ATP attached to it. This dissociation may be important for several reasons. Nature kills several flies with the same blow. The viscosity decreases, and this makes rearrangement of structure possible without much inner friction. At the same time the forces which linked actin to myosin are freed and may be used for the readsorption of liberated K^+ or ATP, the liberation of which was instrumental in excitation. Banga has found that the addition of actin to myosin in the presence of KCl increased the pH up to the color change of phenolphthalein. Evidently some potassium is expelled from its adsorption.* The difference between the adsorbing power of free myosin and myosin linked to actin is not very considerable, as

*This reaction may be involved in the initial rise of pH in muscular contraction, described by Dubuisson.

shown by W. Sz. Herman, but may all the same facilitate readsorption and hereby return to rest.

After the myosin particles are hydrated and have stretched again and the G-actin polymerized to F-actin and united with myosin to F-actomyosin, all will be set for a new contraction.

The Cycle of Contraction

If we now take a bird's eyeview of the cycle of contract-tion at many points we still find large gaps in our knowl-edge. At these points progress only consists of our being able to express our ignorance in more exact terms than before, which is usually the first step towards advance-ment. The difficulty begins with a basic state of rest. At the moment it is impossible to say whether resting muscle contains relaxed actomyosin or contains dissociated acto-myosin, or more exactly actin and myosin side by side. This statement seems to be in contradiction to our experience with actomyosin threads, according to which in the presence of ATP actomyosin is either dissociated or contracted, no relaxed actomyosin being possible at room temperature if ATP is present. The reason for this uncertainty lies in the fact that we are unable to reproduce conditions of the muscle fibre in our actomyosin threads. If we add ATP to the thread the solution will always con-tain some free nucleotide which will react with the protin. In the muscle fibre there is no free ATP. All is adsorbed to the skeleton and the protin is free of it. We do not know what such myosin would do with actin; whether it will be capable of forming relaxed actomyosin at room temperature or not.

The uncertainty about "rest" is increased by Prof. F. B. Straub who thinks that resting muscle may contain its actin in globular form. Should this be so, then excitation would have to bring about the association of globular actin to fibrous actin. The formation of fibrous actin could be followed spontaneously by the formation of actomyosin and the consecutive discharge and contraction. Certainly, Professor Straub has shown that the association of actin is a subtle process and slight changes in ionic balance and charge may have trigger-action, so until the measurements of double refraction, x-ray data or other physical constants do not allow this possibility to be excluded, we have to take it into account. If muscle contains fibrous actin and myosin side by side, excitation would have to bring about association by decreasing critical charges. If resting muscle contains actomyosin, excitation will simply have to bring about discharge and consecutive shortening.

Gerendás and Szarvas have lately produced evidence in favor of the view that resting muscle contains F-actomyosin, contains therefore its actin in F form, and contains its actin and myosin associated to actomyosin. They have shown that Q bands of resting muscle show the UV spectrum of F-actomyosin and not that of actin plus myosin. Until this observation is corroborated and until we definitely know what rest means, we cannot say either what excitation really is and cannot replace this mysterious word by more exact terms. At any rate, we have seen that resting muscle is a very metastable system balanced on a razor's edge, which might be "excited" and brought to contraction in many different ways. The liberation of minute quantities of ATP adsorbed to the skeleton might bring about the change, or the change may be brought about by diluting the fluid or by knocking off, in one way or another, a few ions from myosin lowering the charge below the typical level. Such actions may be coupled and ATP may be released by the loss of a few potassium ions which have kept it adsorbed. It is even believable that an electric field may produce contraction by shifting charges within the myosin particle. It is even possible that the rearrangements taking place in one micell may upset conditions in its neighbor, making excitation self propagating.

A more rounded picture can be made of energy changes. It has been shown that the contracted state is a more stable one, contraction being a spontaneous process, going hand in hand with a decrease in free energy. At 37°C. the $\triangle$ F is 7-8000 calories. The myosin uses its own inner energy to do work. This change is probably induced by the coupling of ATP to the protin. In the contracted state the system becomes enzymatically active, and the myosin particle splits the phosphate link of ATP, liberating 11,000 calories of free energy. 7-8000 cal. of this will be used to bring the system back to its higher energy level and the net loss, the decrease in free energy of the system, will be 4,000 calories, a waste which we can permit. Thus both processes, contraction and relaxation, are spontaneous processes involving a decrease of the free energy of the system, relaxation following contraction automatically.

Rigor and Contracture

The ATP, adsorbed to myosin, has a profound effect on the physical properties of its actomyosin. Not only does this ATP make actomyosin capable of changes which we described as dissociation, contraction and relaxation, but also it was described by Engelhardt, Ljubimova and Meitina that ATP increases the extensibility of "myosin" threads in a specific way. This discovery was, in fact, the first specific effect of ATP on myosin. Similar results have been obtained lately by Buchthal, Deutsch, Knappeis and Petersen. ATP makes actomyosin plastic, supple, while without ATP actomyosin is rigid. In presence of physiological salt concentrations ATP-free actomyosin must be discharged, thus not only rigid but also slightly contracted.

It is possible to predict what will happen if the ATP is decomposed in an unexcited muscle, as is the case after death: we would be left with a rigid, salt-precipitated and therefore slightly contracted actomyosin. Precipitation (discharge, dehydration) means contraction, but in the absence of ATP these effects are very weak, and contraction will be very moderate. The actomyosin without ATP will be rather rigid. This condition is *rigor mortis*. T. Erdös studied the relation of the development of rigor and the ATP concentration and the two curves were perfect mirror images. As the ATP disappears, the rigor sets in. The process starts at once after death which shows that the whole physiological ATP concentration is needed to keep the muscle in fully relaxed state.

The situation will be different if ATP is decomposed in an excitable muscle. Increase of ATP concentration favors relaxation, while decrease favors contraction. Less ATP is needed to make the muscle contract than is necessary to make it relax and decrease of ATP widens the zone of contraction. So we may expect that as the ATP disappears the relaxation becomes more and more incomplete and the muscle ends up in contracture. This is what Erdös found while studying the physical state of muscle as compared with its ATP concentration. The results were less regular than in the case of rigor, but still definite enough to show the relation in a number of different contractures, like that produced by monoiodoacetic acid, chloroform vapor, caffeine, or excessive labor. Here, too, the physical change sets in as soon as the ATP concentration begins to fall below its physiological level.

These measurements posed the question whether certain cases of human pathology, characterized by deficient relaxation of muscle cells, is not due to a lack of ATP. At Szeged's medical clinic, Profs. S. Rusznyak, Hamori applied ATP in cases of vasospastic gangrenes (thromboangütis obliterans), where the spastic condition of muscle cells in arterioles blocked the flow of the blood making the limb die. ATP was administered to patients who were assigned to amputation. The limbs were saved and patients discharged as cured. I am unable to say whether the effect was permanent.

Other conditions were dysmenorrheas, where increased tonus of the uterus made menorrhea painful. The pains were relieved by ATP. Very encouraging results were obtained in angina pectoris; during treatment patients seemed to be free of attacks. More extensive and systematic research along these lines is indicated.

Smooth Muscle, Heart Muscle

The reactions of smooth and heart muscle are in many ways greatly different from those of cross-striated muscle and the question is whether the difference lies in the basic mechanism of contraction or in higher levels of organization and regulation. G. Rózsa prepared myosin and actin from these muscles and then prepared actomyosin from them, added ATP and salts, measured limits of dissociation and contraction, but could find no difference in behavior among the three muscles. He also interchanged cross-striated actin with smooth-muscle actin and myosin, etc.; they all reacted the same. This indicates that the basic contractile mechanism in all kinds of muscle is the same only the superimposed regulations being different.

Recently, A. Csapó studied the actomyosin of uterus in the course of pregnancy. The smooth muscle of the uterus becomes progressively more and more reactive in the course of being gravid. Csapó showed that the same was true for actomyosin prepared from the pregnant uterus and the change could be correlated to the actin content which rose as pregnancy advanced. At the moment it would be premature to say any more than that this line of work opens hopeful alleys to clinical pathology.

I have come to my journey's end and now you probably expect me to finish my lecture in a dramatic way by telling you what life is. I am afraid my lectures will just fizzle out and I will be unable to tell what life is.

In our discussion we have passed several levels of organization from electrons to bands, from bands to molecules and micells, from micells to filaments and fibrils, up to the muscle fibre. There are many more levels above this. At the next level, we have nerves and blood circulation coming in, then the reflex arc, the brain cortex, and in the end the whole rabbit, but I doubt whether the list is herewith complete. Everyone knows this much of biology——that one rabbit could never reproduce itself, and if life is characterized by self-reproduction, one rabbit could not be called alive at all, and one rabbit is no rabbit, and only two rabbits are one rabbit, and so we may go on calling in the end only the whole of living nature alive.

At the level which concerned us most, the level of the actomyosin filament, life seems to be connected with the existence of two levels of energy which correspond with two different physical states and the two basic functional states of living matter: rest and activity.

In stepping up from one level to the other we always gain in qualities because the whole is always more than its parts. But we not only gain, we also lose, as functions become more specialized and adapted, scopes more limited.

We may walk the same way in the opposite direction going down in the scale of organization, and everywhere we will find signs of life, though less and less complete, until we are left in the end with atoms and electrons, which may still have some properties of life. Whether something is alive or not depends on our idea of what we call "alive" and what criterion we choose. The noun "life" has no sense, there being no such thing.

There is no definite answer to our question. We may stop at every level of organization and draw the limit where we want to. It depends upon the view we take. Judges, for instance, do not excuse shooting through a man's head if told that only the most superfluous level of organization was touched and that there are plenty of levels and plenty of life left below. For them the limit is the complete individual. The elementary happenings, however, seem to take place in the dimensions of the electrons and their band structures, and all that splendor and wealth of living nature is built up of reactions which we might hope, some day, to be able to describe with equations of quantum mechanics.

Biochemists as a rule have a destructive mind. They are happier and think to understand the living machine better when they have succeeded in dismantling it into the smallest pieces. I want to address myself especially to my younger colleagues present, who are headed for a research career, making their vocation an adventure into the unknown. Do not limit your attention to bits only; go both ways. Try to understand the whole and stop at every level and look about most carefully, for at every level you will find surprises. It does not matter which level we work at, they are all equally wonderful; but we must know where we are, which level we are talking about, and not draw unwarranted conclusions either upwards or downwards. When I address you the next time, I hope to be able to finish my lecture in a more dramatic way, by pulling a synthetic rabbit out of my pocket.

ILLUSTRATIONS

LIST OF ILLUSTRATIONS

PLATE I

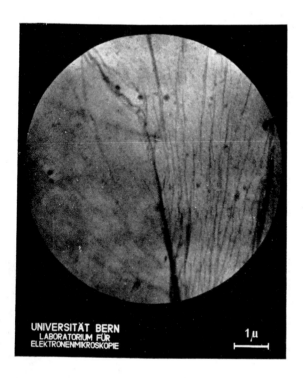

Fig. 1a   Fig. 1b

Fig. 1a.   EM photography of a fibril from a cross-striated muscle of the rabbit, loosened by supersonic radiation.

Fig. 1b.   EM picture of filament isolated by means of supersonic radiation.   Gold shadowed.   1 : 30,000 (1mm. = 330A).

PLATE II

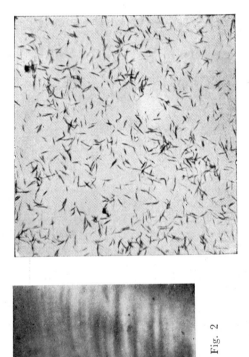

Fig. 5. Myosin crystals. Magnification 1:90.

Fig. 2

Fig. 2. Fibrous actin flowing through a capillary under periodic impulses, and showing cross-striation.

PLATE III

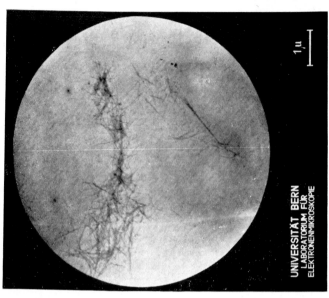

Fig. 6b. EM picture of microcrystals of myosin.

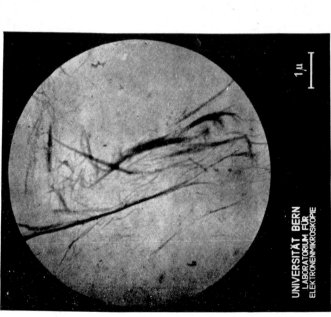

Fig. 6a. EM picture of "myosin crystals."

PLATE IV

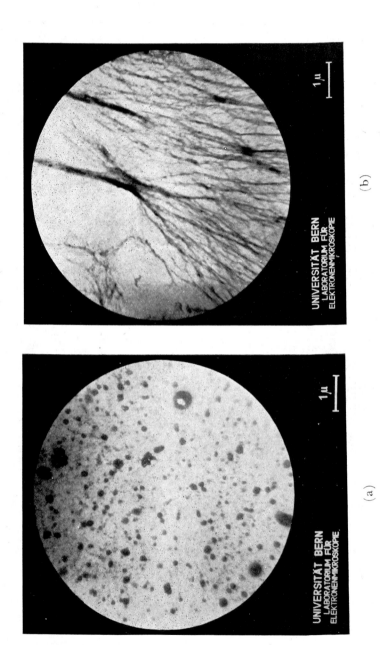

(a)   (b)

Fig. 11   EM picture of globular actin (a) and the same actin a few minutes after the addition of 0.1 M

PLATE V

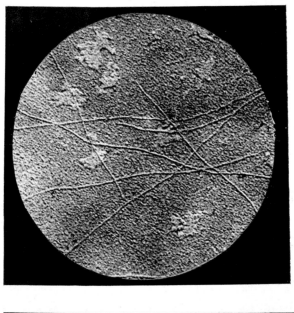

Fig. 13. EM picture of fibrous actin. Gold-shadowed. 1:27,000.

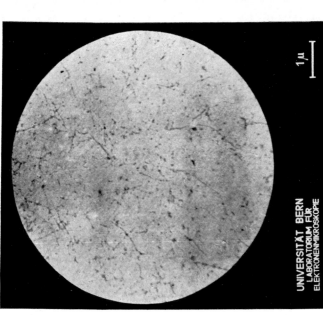

UNIVERSITÄT BERN
LABORATORIUM FÜR
ELEKTRONENMIKROSKOPE

1 μ

Fig. 12. EM picture of actin in the process of polymerization.

PLATE VI

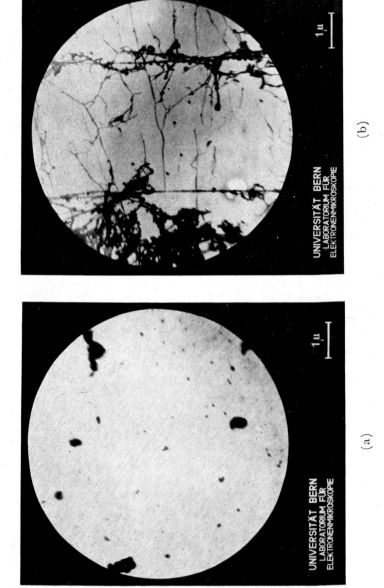

(a)

(b)

Fig. 14. (a) The fibrous actin of Fig. 11b after 10 minutes' treatment with supersonic waves. (b) Same

PLATE VII

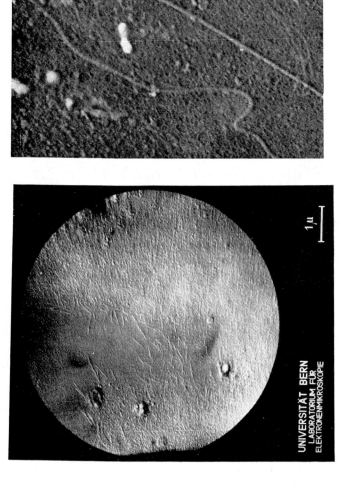

Fig. 15. EM picture of actin polymerized to
short rodlets. Slightly gold-shadowed.

Fig. 16. EM picture of actomyosin
1:22,000.

THIS VOLUME MAY CIRCULATE FOR 2 WEEKS
Renewals May Be Made In Person Or By Phone:
x 5300; from outside 472-5300

DATE DUE	DATE RETURNED

99427